Riverby Edition

THE WRITINGS OF
JOHN BURROUGHS

WITH PORTRAITS AND MANY ILLUSTRATIONS

VOLUME XII

Mr. Burroughs watching a Bird

THE WRITINGS

OF

JOHN BURROUGHS

XII

WAYS OF NATURE

BOSTON AND NEW YORK

HOUGHTON MIFFLIN COMPANY

The Riverside Press, Cambridge

PS
1220
E95
v.12

PREFACE

My reader will find this volume quite a departure in certain ways from the tone and spirit of my previous books, especially in regard to the subject of animal intelligence. Heretofore I have made the most of every gleam of intelligence of bird or four-footed beast that came under my observation, often, I fancy, making too much of it, and giving the wild creatures credit for more "sense" than they really possessed. The nature lover is always tempted to do this very thing; his tendency is to humanize the wild life about him, and to read his own traits and moods into whatever he looks upon. I have never consciously done this myself, at least to the extent of willfully misleading my reader. But some of our later nature writers have been guilty of this fault, and have so grossly exaggerated and misrepresented the every-day wild life of our fields and woods that their example has caused a strong reaction to take place in my own mind, and has led me to set about examining the whole subject of animal life and instinct in a way I have never done before.

In March, 1903, I contributed to "The Atlantic Monthly" a paper called "Real and Sham Natural History," which was as vigorous a protest as I could make against the growing tendency to humanize the lower animals. The paper was widely read and discussed, and bore fruit in many ways, much of it good and wholesome fruit, but a little of it bitter and acrid. For obvious reasons that paper is not included in this collection. But I have given all the essays that were the outcome of the currents of thought and inquiry that it set going in my mind, and I have given them nearly in the order in which they were written, so that the reader may see the growth of my own mind and opinions in relation to the subject. I confess I have not been fully able to persuade myself that the lower animals ever show anything more than a faint gleam of what we call thought and reflection, — the power to evolve ideas from sense impressions, — except feebly in the case of the dog and the apes, and possibly the elephant. Nearly all the animal behavior that the credulous public looks upon as the outcome of reason is simply the result of the adaptiveness and plasticity of instinct. The animal has impulses and impressions where we have ideas and concepts. Of our faculties I concede to them perception, sense memory, and association of memories, and little else. Without these it would be impossible for their lives to go on.

I am aware that there is much repetition in this volume, and that the names of several of the separate chapters differ much more than do the subjects discussed in them.

PREFACE

When I was a boy on the farm, we used to thrash our grain with the hand-flail. Our custom was to thrash a flooring of sheaves on one side, then turn the sheaves over and thrash them on the other, then unbind them and thrash the loosened straw again, and then finish by turning the whole over and thrashing it once more. I suspect my reader will feel that I have followed the same method in many of these papers. I have thrashed the same straw several times, but I have turned it each time, and I trust have been rewarded by a few additional grains of truth.

Let me hope that the result of the discussion or thrashing will not be to make the reader love the animals less, but rather to love the truth more.

June, 1905.

CONTENTS

LIST OF ILLUSTRATIONS

I

WAYS OF NATURE

I WAS much amused lately by a half-dozen or more letters that came to me from some Californian schoolchildren, who wrote to ask if I would please tell them whether or not birds have sense. One little girl said: "I would be pleased if you would write and tell me if birds have sense. I wanted to see if I could n't be the first one to know." I felt obliged to reply to the children that we ourselves do not have sense enough to know just how much sense the birds and other wild creatures do have, and that they do appear to have some, though their actions are probably the result of what we call instinct, or natural prompting, like that of the bean-stalk when it climbs the pole. Yet a bean-stalk will sometimes show a kind of perversity or depravity that looks like the result of deliberate choice. Each season, among my dozen or more hills of pole-beans, there are usually two or three low-minded plants that will not climb the poles, but go groveling upon the ground, wandering off among the potato-vines or cucumbers, departing utterly from the traditions of their race, becoming shiftless and vagrant. When

1

I lift them up and wind them around the poles and
tie them with a wisp of grass, they rarely stay. In
some way they seem to get a wrong start in life, or
else are degenerates from the first. I have never
known anything like this among the wild creatures,
though it happens often enough among our own
kind. The trouble with the bean is doubtless this:
the Lima bean is of South American origin, and in
the Southern Hemisphere, beans, it seems, go the
other way around the pole; that is, from right to
left. When transferred north of the equator, it takes
them some time to learn the new way, or from left to
right, and a few of them are always backsliding,
or departing from the new way and vaguely seeking
the old; and not finding this, they become vaga-
bonds.

How much or how little sense or judgment our
wild neighbors have is hard to determine. The
crows and other birds that carry shell-fish high in
the air and then let them drop upon the rocks to
break the shell show something very much like
reason, or a knowledge of the relation of cause and
effect, though it is probably an unthinking habit
formed in their ancestors under the pressure of
hunger. Froude tells of some species of bird that
he saw in South Africa flying amid the swarm of
migrating locusts and clipping off the wings of the
insects so that they would drop to the earth, where
the birds could devour them at their leisure. Our

squirrels will cut off the chestnut burs before they have opened, allowing them to fall to the ground, where, as they seem to know, the burs soon dry open. Feed a caged coon soiled food, — a piece of bread or meat rolled on the ground, — and before he eats it he will put it in his dish of water and wash it off. The author of "Wild Life Near Home" says that muskrats "will wash what they eat, whether washing is needed or not." If the coon washes his food only when it needs washing, and not in every individual instance, then the proceeding looks like an act of judgment ; the same with the muskrat. But if they always wash their food, whether soiled or not, the act looks more like instinct or an inherited habit, the origin of which is obscure.

Birds and animals probably think without knowing that they think; that is, they have not self-consciousness. Only man seems to be endowed with this faculty; he alone develops disinterested intelligence, — intelligence that is not primarily concerned with his own safety and well-being, but that looks abroad upon things. The wit of the lower animals seems all to have been developed by the struggle for existence, and it rarely gets beyond the prudential stage. The sharper the struggle, the sharper the wit. Our porcupine, for instance, is probably the most stupid of animals and has the least speed ; it has little use for either wit or celerity of movement. It carries a death-dealing armor to protect it from its enemies, and it can climb the nearest hemlock tree and live on the bark all winter. The skunk, too, pays for its terrible weapon by dull wits. But think of the wit of the much-hunted fox, the much-hunted otter, the much-sought beaver! Even the grouse, when often fired at, learns, when it is started in the open, to fly with a corkscrew motion to avoid the shot.

Fear, love, and hunger were the agents that developed the wits of the lower animals, as they were, of course, the prime factors in developing the intelligence of man. But man has gone on, while the animals have stopped at these fundamental wants, — the need of safety, of offspring, of food.

Probably in a state of wild nature birds never make mistakes, but where they come in contact wit.. our civilization and are confronted by new conditions, they very naturally make mistakes. For instance, their cunning in nest-building sometimes deserts them. The art of the bird is to conceal its nest both as to position and as to material, but now and then it is betrayed into weaving into its structure showy and bizarre bits of this or that, which give its secret away, and which seem to violate all the traditions of its kind. I have the picture of a robin's nest before me, upon the outside of which are stuck a muslin flower, a leaf from a small calendar, and a photograph of a local celebrity. A more incongruous use of material in bird architecture it would be hard to find. I have been told of another robin's nest upon the outside of which the bird had fastened a wooden label from a near-by flower-bed, marked "Wake Robin." Still another nest I have seen built upon a large, showy foundation of the paper-like flowers of antennaria, or everlasting. The wood thrush frequently weaves a fragment of newspaper or a white rag into the foundation of its nest. "Evil communications corrupt good manners." The newspaper and the rag-bag unsettle the wits of the birds. The phœbe-bird is capable of this kind of mistake or indiscretion. All the past generations of her tribe have built upon natural and, therefore, neutral sites, usually under shelving and overhanging rocks, and the art of adapting the nest to its surroundings, blending it with them, has been highly developed. But phœbe now frequently builds under our sheds and porches, where, so far as concealment is concerned, a change of material, say from moss to dry grass or shreds of bark, would be an advantage to her ; but she departs not a bit from the family traditions ; she uses the same woodsy mosses, which in some cases, especially when the nest is placed upon newly sawed timber, make her secret an open one to all eyes.

It does indeed often look as if the birds had very little sense. Think of a bluebird, or an oriole, or a robin, or a jay, fighting for hours at a time its own image as reflected in a pane of glass; quite exhaust-

ing itself in its fury to demolish its supposed rival?
Yet I have often witnessed this little comedy. It is
another instance of how the arts of our civilization
corrupt and confuse the birds. It may be that in the
course of many generations the knowledge of glass
will get into their blood, and they will cease to be
fooled by it, as they may also in time learn what a
poor foundation the newspaper is to build upon.
The ant or the bee could not be fooled by the glass
in that way for a moment.

Have the birds and our other wild neighbors
sense, as distinguished from instinct? Is a change
of habits to meet new conditions, or the taking
advantage of accidental circumstances, an evidence
of sense? How many birds appear to have taken
advantage of the protection afforded by man in
building their nests! How many of them build
near paths and along roadsides, to say nothing of
those that come close to our dwellings! Even the
quail seems to prefer the borders of the highway
to the open fields. I have chanced upon only three
quails' nests, and these were all by the roadside.
One season a scarlet tanager that had failed with
her first nest in the woods came to try again in a
little cherry tree that stood in the open, a few feet
from my cabin, where I could almost touch the nest
with my hand as I passed. But in my absence she
again came to grief, some marauder, probably a
red squirrel, taking her eggs. Will her failure in

this case cause her to lose faith in the protective influence of the shadow of a human dwelling? I hope
not. I have known the turtle dove to make a similar move, occupying an old robin's nest near my
neighbor's cottage. The timid rabbit will sometimes
come up from the bushy fields and excavate a place
for her nest in the lawn a few feet from the house.
All such things look like acts of judgment, though
they may be only the result of a greater fear overcoming a lesser fear.

It is in the preservation of their lives and of their
young that the wild creatures come the nearest to
showing what we call sense or reason. The boys tell
me that a rabbit that has been driven from her hole
a couple of times by a ferret will not again run into
it when pursued. The tragedy of a rabbit pursued
by a mink or a weasel may often be read upon our
winter snows. The rabbit does not take to her hole;
it would be fatal. And yet, though capable of far
greater speed, so far as I have observed, she does not
escape the mink; he very soon pulls her down. It
would look as though a fatal paralysis, the paralysis
of utter fear, fell upon the poor creature as soon
as she found herself hunted by this subtle, blood-
thirsty enemy. I have seen upon the snow where her
jumps had become shorter and shorter, with tufts
of fur marking each stride, till the bloodstains,
and then her half-devoured body, told the whole
tragic story.

There is probably nothing in human experience, at this age of the world, that is like the helpless terror that seizes the rabbits as it does other of our lesser wild creatures, when pursued by any of the weasel tribe. They seem instantly to be under some fatal spell which binds their feet and destroys their will power. It would seem as if a certain phase of nature from which we get our notions of fate and cruelty had taken form in the weasel.

The rabbit, when pursued by the fox or by the dog, quickly takes to hole. Hence, perhaps, the wit of the fox that a hunter told me about. The story was all written upon the snow. A mink was hunting a rabbit, and the fox, happening along, evidently took in the situation at a glance. He secreted himself behind a tree or a rock, and, as the rabbit came along, swept her from her course like a charge of shot fired at close range, hurling her several feet over the snow, and then seizing her and carrying her to his den up the mountain-side.

It would be interesting to know how long our chimney swifts saw the open chimney-stacks of the early settlers beneath them before they abandoned the hollow trees in the woods and entered the chimneys for nesting and roosting purposes. Was the act an act of judgment, or simply an unreasoning impulse, like so much else in the lives of the wild creatures?

In the choice of nesting-material the swift shows

no change of habit. She still snips off the small dry twigs from the tree-tops and glues them together, and to the side of the chimney, with her own glue. The soot is a new obstacle in her way, that she does not yet seem to have learned to overcome, as the rains often loosen it and cause her nest to fall to the bottom. She has a pretty way of trying to frighten you off when your head suddenly darkens the opening above her. At such times she leaves the nest and clings to the side of the chimney near it. Then, slowly raising her wings, she suddenly springs out from the wall and back again, making as loud a drumming with them in the passage as she is capable of. If this does not frighten you away, she repeats it three or four times. If your face still hovers above her, she remains quiet and watches you.

What a creature of the air this bird is, never touching the ground, so far as I know, and never tasting earthly food! The swallow does perch now and then and descend to the ground for nesting-material; but the swift, I have reason to believe, even outrides the summer storms, facing them on steady wing, high in air. The twigs for her nest she gathers on the wing, sweeping along like children on a "merry-go-round" who try to seize a ring, or to do some other feat, as they pass a given point. If the swift misses the twig, or it fails to yield to her the first time, she tries again and again, each time making a wider circuit, as if to tame and train her steed a little and bring him up more squarely to the mark next time.

The swift is a stiff flyer: there appear to be no joints in her wings; she suggests something made of wires or of steel. Yet the air of frolic and of superabundance of wing-power is more marked with her than with any other of our birds. Her feeding and twig-gathering seem like asides in a life of endless play. Several times both in spring and fall I have seen swifts gather in immense numbers toward nightfall, to take refuge in large unused chimney-stacks. On such occasions they seem to be coming together for some aerial festival or grand celebration; and, as if bent upon a final effort to work off a part of their superabundant wing-power before settling down for the night, they circle and circle high above the chimney-top, a great cloud of them, drifting this way and that, all in high spirits and chippering as they fly. Their numbers constantly increase as other members of the clan come dashing in from all points of the compass. Swifts seem to materialize out of empty air on all sides of the chippering, whirling ring, as an hour or more this assembling of the clan and this flight festival go on. The birds must gather in from whole counties, or from half a State. They have been on the wing all day, and yet now they seem as tireless as the wind, and as if unable to curb their powers.

One fall they gathered in this way and took refuge

for the night in a large chimney-stack in a city near me, for more than a month and a half. Several times I went to town to witness the spectacle, and a spectacle it was: ten thousand of them, I should think, filling the air above a whole square like a whirling swarm of huge black bees, but saluting the ear with a multitudinous chippering, instead of a humming. People gathered upon the sidewalks to see them. It was a rare circus performance, free to all. After a great many feints and playful approaches, the whirling ring of birds would suddenly grow denser above the chimney; then a stream of them, as if drawn down by some power of suction, would pour into the opening. For only a few seconds would this downward rush continue; then, as if the spirit of frolic had again got the upper hand of them, the ring would rise, and the chippering and circling go on. In a minute or two the same manœuvre would be repeated, the chimney, as it were, taking its swallows at intervals to prevent choking. It usually took a half-hour or more for the birds all to disappear down its capacious throat. There was always an air of timidity and irresolution about their approach to the chimney, just as there always is about their approach to the dead tree-top from which they procure their twigs for nest-building. Often did I see birds hesitate above the opening and then pass on, apparently as though they had not struck it at just the right angle. On one occasion a solitary bird was left flying, and it took three or four trials either to make up its mind or to catch the trick of the descent. On dark or threatening or stormy days the birds would begin to assemble by mid-afternoon, and by four or five o'clock were all in their lodgings.

The chimney is a capacious one, forty or fifty feet high and nearly three feet square, yet it did not seem adequate to afford breathing-space for so many birds. I was curious to know how they disposed themselves inside. At the bottom was a small opening. Holding my ear to it, I could hear a continuous chippering and humming, as if the birds were still all in motion, like an agitated beehive. At nine o'clock this multitudinous sound of wings and voices was still going on, and doubtless it was kept up all night. What was the meaning of it? Was the press of birds so great that they needed to keep their wings moving to ventilate the shaft, as do certain of the bees in a crowded hive? Or were these restless spirits unable to fold their wings even in sleep? I was very curious to get a peep inside that chimney when the swifts were in it. So one afternoon this opportunity was afforded me by the removal of the large smoke-pipe of the old steam-boiler. This left an opening into which I could thrust my head and shoulders. The sound of wings and voices filled the hollow shaft. On looking up, I saw the sides of the chimney for about half its length paved with the restless birds; they sat so close together that their bodies touched. Moreover, a large number of them were constantly on the wing, showing against the sky light as if they were leaving the chimney. But they did not leave it. They rose up a few feet and then resumed their positions upon the sides, and it was this movement that caused the humming sound. All the while the droppings of the birds came down like a summer shower. At the bottom of the shaft was a mine of guano three or four feet deep, with a dead swift here and there upon it. Probably one or more birds out of such a multitude died every night. I had fancied there would be many more. It was a long time before it dawned upon me what this uninterrupted flight within the chimney meant. Finally I saw that it was a sanitary measure: only thus could the birds keep from soiling each other with their droppings. Birds digest very rapidly, and had they all continued to cling to the sides of the wall, they would have been in a sad predicament before morning. Like other acts of cleanliness on the part of birds, this was doubtless the prompting of instinct and not of judgment. It was Nature looking out for her own.

In view, then, of the doubtful sense or intelligence of the wild creatures, what shall we say of the new school of nature writers or natural history romancers that has lately arisen, and that reads into the birds and animals almost the entire human psychology? This, surely: so far as these writers awaken an interest in the wild denizens of the field and wood, and foster a genuine love of them in the hearts of the young people, so far is their influence good; but so far as they pervert natural history and give false impressions of the intelligence of our animals, catering to a taste that prefers the fanciful to the true and the real, is their influence bad. Of course the great army of readers prefer this sugar-coated natural history to the real thing, but the danger always is that an indulgence of this taste will take away a liking for the real thing, or prevent its development. The knowing ones, those who can take these pretty tales with the pinch of salt of real knowledge, are not many; the great majority are simply entertained while they are being humbugged. There may be no very serious objection to the popular love of sweets being catered to in this field by serving up the life-history of our animals in a story, all the missing links supplied, and all their motives and acts humanized, provided it is not done covertly and under the guise of a real history. We are never at a loss how to take Kipling in his "Jungle Book;" we are pretty sure that this is fact dressed up as fiction, and that much of the real life of the jungle is in these stories. I remember reading his story of "The White Seal" shortly after I had visited the Seal Islands in Bering Sea, and I could not detect in the story one departure from the facts of the life-history of the seal, so far as it is known. Kipling takes no covert liberties with

natural history, any more than he does with the facts
of human history in his novels.

Unadulterated, unsweetened observations are
what the real nature-lover craves. No man can
invent incidents and traits as interesting as the
reality. Then, to know that a thing is true gives it
such a savor! The truth — how we do crave the
truth! We cannot feed our minds on simulacra any
more than we can our bodies. Do assure us that the
thing you tell is true. If you must counterfeit the
truth, do it so deftly that we shall never detect you.
But in natural history there is no need to counterfeit the truth; the reality always suffices, if you
have eyes to see it and ears to hear it. Behold what
Maeterlinck makes out of the life of the bee, simply by getting at and portraying the facts — a true
wonder-book, the enchantment of poetry wedded
to the authority of science.

Works on animal intelligence, such as Romanes's,
abound in incidents that show in the animals reason
and forethought in their simpler forms; but in many
cases the incidents related in these works are not
well authenticated, nor told by trained observers.
The observations of the great majority of people
have no scientific value whatever. Romanes quotes
from some person who alleges that he saw a pair of
nightingales, during a flood in the river near which
their nest was placed, pick up the nest bodily and
carry it to a place of safety. This is incredible. If

Romanes himself or Darwin himself said he saw this, one would have to believe it. Birds whose nests have been plundered sometimes pull the old nest to pieces and use the material, or parts of it, in building a new nest; but I cannot believe that any pair of birds ever picked up a nest containing eggs and carried it off to a new place. How could they do it? With one on each side, how could they fly with the nest between them? They could not carry it with their feet, and how could they manage it with their beaks?

My neighbor met in the woods a black snake that had just swallowed a red squirrel. Now your romance-naturalist may take such a fact as this and make as pretty a story of it as he can. He may ascribe to the snake and his victim all the human emotions he pleases. He may make the snake glide through the tree-tops from limb to limb, and from tree to tree, in pursuit of its prey: the main thing is, the snake got the squirrel. If our romancer makes the snake fascinate the squirrel, I shall object, because I don't believe that snakes have this power. People like to believe that they have. It would seem as if this subtle, gliding, hateful creature ought to have some such mysterious gift, but I have no proof that it has. Every year I see the black snake robbing birds'-nests, or pursued by birds whose nests it has just plundered, but I have yet to see it cast its fatal spell upon a grown bird. Or, if our romancer says that the black snake was drilled in the art of squirrel-catching by its mother, I shall know he is a pretender.

Speaking of snakes reminds me of an incident I have several times witnessed in our woods in connection with a snake commonly called the sissing or blowing adder. When I have teased this snake a few moments with my cane, it seems to be seized with an epileptic or cataleptic fit. It throws itself upon its back, coiled nearly in the form of a figure eight, and begins a series of writhings and twistings and convulsive movements astonishing to behold. Its mouth is open and presently full of leaf-mould, its eyes are covered with the same, its head is thrown back, its white belly up; now it is under the leaves, now out, the body all the while being rapidly drawn through this figure eight, so that the head and tail are constantly changing place. What does it mean? Is it fear? Is it a real fit? I do not know, but any one of our romance-naturalists could tell you at once. I can only suggest that it may be a ruse to baffle its enemy, the black snake, when he would attempt to crush it in his folds, or to seize its head when he would swallow it.

I am reminded of another mystery connected with a snake, or a snake-skin, and a bird. Why does our great crested flycatcher weave a snake-skin into its nest, or, in lieu of that, something that suggests a snake-skin, such as an onion-skin, or fish-scales, or a bit of oiled paper? It is thought by some persons

17

that it uses the snake-skin as a kind of scarecrow, to frighten away its natural enemies. But think what this purpose in the use of it would imply. It would imply that the bird knew that there were among its enemies creatures that were afraid of snakes — so afraid of them that one of their faded and cast-of skins would keep these enemies away. How could the bird obtain this knowledge? It is not afraid of the skin itself; why should it infer that squirrels, for instance, are? I am convinced there is nothing in this notion. In all the nests that have come under my observation, the snake-skin was in faded fragments woven into the texture of the nest, and one would not be aware of its presence unless he pulled the nest to pieces. True, Mr. Frank Bolles reports finding a nest of this bird with a whole snake-skin coiled around a single egg; but it was the skin of a small garter-snake, six or seven inches long, and could not therefore have inspired much terror in the heart of the bird's natural enemies. Dallas Lore Sharp, author of that delightful book, "Wild Life Near Home," tells me he has seen a whole skin dangling nearly its entire length from the hole that contained the nest, just as he has seen strings hanging from the nest of the kingbird. The bird was too hurried or too careless to pull in the skin. Mr. Sharp adds that he cannot "give the bird credit for appreciating the attitude of the rest of the world toward snakes, and making use of the fear." Moreover, a cast-off snake-skin looks very little like a snake. It is thin, shrunken, faded, papery, and there is no terror in it. Then, too, it is dark in the cavity of the nest, consequently the skin could not serve as a scarecrow in any case. Hence, whatever its purpose may be, it surely is not that. It looks like a mere fancy or whim of the bird. There is that in its voice and ways that suggests something a little uncanny. Its call is more like the call of the toad than that of a bird. If the toad did not always swallow its own cast-off skin, the bird would probably use that too.

At the best we can only guess at the motives of the birds and beasts. As I have elsewhere said, they nearly all have reference in some way to the self-preservation of these creatures. But how the bits of an old snake-skin in a bird's nest can contribute specially to this end, I cannot see.

Nature is not always consistent; she does not always choose the best means to a given end. For instance, all the wrens except our house wren seem to use about the best material at hand for their nests. What can be more unsuitable, untractable, for a nest in a hole or cavity than the twigs the house wren uses? Dry grasses or bits of soft bark would bend and adapt themselves easily to the exigencies of the case; but stiff, unyielding twigs! What a contrast to the suitableness of the material the hummingbird uses — the down of some plant, which seems to have a poetic fitness!

Yesterday in my walk I saw where a red squirrel had stripped the soft outer bark off a group of red cedars to build its winter's nest with. This also seemed fit, — fit that such a creature of the trees should not go to the ground for its nest-material, and should choose something soft and pliable. Among the birches, it probably gathers the fine curling shreds of the birch bark.

Beside my path in the woods a downy woodpecker, late one fall, drilled a hole in the top of a small dead black birch for his winter quarters. My attention was first called to his doings by the white chips upon the ground. Every day as I passed I would rap upon his tree, and if he was in he would appear at his door and ask plainly enough what I wanted now. One day when I rapped, something else appeared at the door — I could not make out what. I continued my rapping, when out came two flying-squirrels. On the tree being given a vigorous shake, it broke off at the hole, and the squirrels went sliding down the air to the foot of a hemlock, up which they disappeared. They had dispossessed Downy of his house, had carried in some grass and leaves for a nest, and were as snug as a bug in a rug. Downy drilled another cell in a dead oak farther up the hill, and, I hope, passed the winter there unmolested. Such incidents, comic or tragic, as they chance to strike us, are happening all about us, if we have eyes to see them.

The next season, near sundown of a late November day, I saw Downy trying to get possession of a hole not his own. I chanced to be passing under a maple, when white chips upon the ground again caused me to scrutinize the branches overhead. Just then I saw Downy come to the tree, and, hopping around on the under side of a large dry limb, begin to make passes at something with his beak. Presently I made out a round hole there, with something in it returning Downy's thrusts. The sparring continued some moments. Downy would hop away a few feet, then return to the attack, each time to be met by the occupant of the hole. I suspected an English sparrow had taken possession of Downy's cell in his absence during the day, but I was wrong. Downy flew to another branch, and I tossed up a stone against the one that contained the hole, when, with a sharp, steely note, out came a hairy woodpecker and alighted on a near-by branch. Downy, then, had the "cheek" to try to turn his large rival out of doors — and it was Hairy's cell, too; one could see that by the size of the entrance. Thus loosely does the rule of *meum* and *tuum* obtain in the woods. There is no moral code in nature. Might reads right. Man in communities has evolved ethical standards of conduct, but nations, in their dealings with one another, are still largely in a state of savage nature, and seek to establish the right, as dogs do, by the appeal to battle.

One season a wood duck laid her eggs in a cavity

in the top of a tall yellow birch near the spring that supplies my cabin with water. A bold climber "shinned" up the fifty or sixty feet of rough tree-trunk and looked in upon the eleven eggs. They were beyond the reach of his arm, in a well-like cavity over three feet deep. How would the mother duck get her young up out of that well and down to the ground? We watched, hoping to see her in the act. But we did not. She may have done it at night or very early in the morning. All we know is that when Amasa one morning passed that way, there sat eleven little tufts of black and yellow down in the spring, with the mother duck near by. It was a pretty sight. The feat of getting down from the tree-top cradle had been safely effected, probably by the young clambering up on the inside walls of the cavity and then tumbling out into the air and coming down gently like huge snowflakes. They are mostly down, and why should they not fall without any danger to life or limb? The notion that the mother duck takes the young one by one in her beak and carries them to the creek is doubtless erroneous. Mr. William Brewster once saw the golden-eye, whose habits of nesting are like those of the wood duck, get its young from the nest to the water in this manner: The mother bird alighted in the water under the nest, looked all around to see that the coast was clear, and then gave a peculiar call. Instantly the young shot out of the cavity that held them, as if the tree had taken an emetic, and came softly down to the water beside their mother. Another observer assures me that he once found a newly hatched duckling hung by the neck in the fork of a bush under a tree in which a brood of wood ducks had been hatched.

The ways of nature, — who can map them, or fathom them, or interpret them, or do much more than read a hint correctly here and there? Of one thing we may be pretty certain, namely, that the ways of wild nature may be studied in our human ways, inasmuch as the latter are an evolution from the former, till we come to the ethical code, to altruism and self-sacrifice. Here we seem to breathe another air, though probably this code differs no more from the animal standards of conduct than our physical atmosphere differs from that of early geologic time.

Our moral code must in some way have been evolved from our rude animal instincts. It came from within; its possibilities were all in nature. If not, where were they?

I have seen disinterested acts among the birds, or what looked like such, as when one bird feeds the young of another species when it hears them crying for food. But that a bird would feed a grown bird of another species, or even of its own, to keep it from starving, I have my doubts. I am quite positive that mice will try to pull one of their fellows out of a trap, but what the motive is, who shall say? Would the same mice share their last crumb with their fellow if he were starving? That, of course, would be a much nearer approach to the human code, and is too much to expect. Bees will clear their fellows of honey, but whether it be to help them, or to save the honey, is a question.

In my youth I saw a parent weasel seize one of its nearly grown young which I had wounded and carry it across an open barway, in spite of my efforts to hinder it. A friend of mine, who is a careful observer, says he once wounded a shrike so that it fell to the ground, but before he got to it, it recovered itself and flew with difficulty toward some near trees, calling to its mate the while; the mate came and seemed to get beneath the wounded bird and buoy it up, so aiding it that it gained the top of a tall tree, where my friend left it. But in neither instance can we call this helpfulness entirely disinterested, or pure altruism.

Emerson said that he was an endless experimenter with no past at his back. This is just what Nature is. She experiments endlessly, seeking new ways, new modes, new forms, and is ever intent upon breaking away from the past. In this way, as Darwin showed, she attains to new species. She is blind, she gropes her way, she trusts to luck; all her successes are chance hits. Whenever I look over my right shoulder, as I sit at my desk writing these sentences, I see a long shoot of a honeysuckle that came in through a crack of my imperfectly closed window last summer. It came in looking, or rather feeling, for something to cling to. It first dropped down upon a pile of books, then reached off till it struck the window-sill of another large window; along this it crept, its regular leaves standing up like so many pairs of green ears, looking very pretty. Coming to the end of the open way there, it turned to the left and reached out into vacancy, till it struck another window-sill running at right angles to the former; along this it traveled nearly half an inch a day, till it came to the end of that road. Then it ventured out into vacant space again, and pointed straight toward me at my desk, ten feet distant. Day by day it kept its seat upon the window-sill, and stretched out farther and farther, almost beckoning me to give it a lift or to bring it support. I could hardly resist its patient daily appeal. Late in October it had bridged about three feet of the distance that separated us, when, one day, the moment came when it could maintain itself outright in the air no longer, and it fell to the floor. "Poor thing," I said, "your faith was blind, but it was real. You knew there was a support somewhere, and you tried all ways to find it." This is Nature. She goes around the circle, she tries every direction, sure that she will find a way at some point. Animals in cages behave in a similar way, looking for a means of escape. In the vineyard I see the grape-vines reaching out blindly in all directions for some hold for their tendrils. The young arms seize upon one another and tighten their hold as if they had at last found what they were in search of. Stop long enough beside one of the vines, and it will cling to you and run all over you.

Behold the tumble-bug with her ball of dung by the roadside; where is she going with it? She is going anywhere and everywhere; she changes her direction, like the vine, whenever she encounters an obstacle. She only knows that somewhere there is a depression or a hole in which her ball with its egg can rest secure, and she keeps on tumbling about till she finds it, or maybe digs one, or comes to grief by the foot of some careless passer-by. This, again, is Nature's way, randomly and tirelessly seeking her ends. When we look over a large section of history, we see that it is man's way, too, or Nature's way in man. His progress has been a blind groping, the result of endless experimentation, and all his failures and mistakes could not be written in a book. How he has tumbled about with his ball, seeking the right place for it, and how many times has he come to grief! All his successes have been lucky hits: steam, electricity, representative government, printing — how long he groped for them before he found them! There is always and everywhere the Darwinian tendency to variation, to seek new forms, to improve upon the past; and man is under this law, the same as is the rest of nature. One generation of men, like one generation of leaves, becomes the fertilizer of the next; failures only enrich the soil or make smoother the way.

There are so many conflicting forces and interests, and the conditions of success are so complex! If the seed fall here, it will not germinate; if there, it will be drowned or washed away; if yonder, it will find too sharp competition. There are only a few places where it will find all the conditions favorable. Hence the prodigality of Nature in seeds, scattering a thousand for one plant or tree. She is like a hunter shooting at random into every tree or bush, hoping to bring down his game, which he does if his ammunition holds out long enough; or like the British soldier in the Boer War, firing vaguely at an enemy that he does not see. But Nature's ammunition always holds out, and she hits her mark in the end. Her ammunition on our planet is the heat of the sun. When this fails, she will no longer hit the mark or try to hit it.

Let there be a plum tree anywhere with the disease called the "black-knot" upon it, and presently every plum tree in its neighborhood will have black knots. Do you think the germs from the first knot knew where to find the other plum trees? No; the wind carried them in every direction, where the plum trees were not as well as where they were. It was a blind search and a chance hit. So with all seeds and germs. Nature covers all the space, and is bound to hit the mark sooner or later. The sun spills his light indiscriminately into space; a small fraction of his rays hit the earth, and we are warmed. Yet to all intents and purposes it is as if he shone for us alone.

II

BIRD-SONGS

I SUSPECT it requires a special gift of grace to enable one to hear the bird-songs; some new power must be added to the ear, or some obstruction removed. There are not only scales upon our eyes so that we do not see, there are scales upon our ears so that we do not hear. A city woman who had spent much of her time in the country once asked a well-known ornithologist to take her where she could hear the bluebird. "What, never heard the bluebird!" said he. "I have not," said the woman. "Then you will never hear it," said the bird-lover; never hear it with that inward ear that gives beauty and meaning to the note. He could probably have taken her in a few minutes where she could have heard the call or warble of the bluebird; but it would have fallen upon unresponsive ears — upon ears that were not sensitized by love for the birds or associations with them. Bird-songs are not music, properly speaking, but only suggestions of music. A great many people whose attention would be quickly arrested by the same volume of sound made by a musical instrument or by artificial means never

29

hear them at all. The sound of a boy's penny whistle there in the grove or the meadow would separate itself more from the background of nature, and be a greater challenge to the ear, than is the strain of the thrush or the song of the sparrow. There is something elusive, indefinite, neutral, about bird-songs that makes them strike obliquely, as it were, upon the ear ; and we are very apt to miss them. They are a part of nature, the Nature that lies about us, entirely occupied with her own affairs, and quite regardless of our presence. Hence it is with bird-songs as it is with so many other things in nature — they are what we make them; the ear that hears them must be half creative. I am always disturbed when persons not especially observant of birds ask me to take them where they can hear a particular bird, in whose song they have become interested through a description in some book. As I listen with them, I feel like apologizing for the bird : it has a bad cold, or has just heard some depressing news; it will not let itself out. The song seems so casual and minor when you make a dead set at it. I have taken persons to hear the hermit thrush, and I have fancied that they were all the time saying to themselves, "Is that all ?" But should one hear the bird in his walk, when the mind is attuned to simple things and is open and receptive, when expectation is not aroused and the song comes as a surprise out of the dusky silence of the woods, then one feels that it merits all the fine things that can be said of it.

One of our popular writers and lecturers upon birds told me this incident: He had engaged to take two city girls out for a walk in the country, to teach them the names of the birds they might see and hear. Before they started, he read to them Henry van Dyke's poem on the song sparrow, — one of our best bird-poems, — telling them that the song sparrow was one of the first birds they were likely to hear. As they proceeded with their walk, sure enough, there by the roadside was a sparrow in song. The bird man called the attention of his companions to it. It was some time before the unpracticed ears of the girls could make it out; then one of them said (the poem she had just heard, I suppose, still ringing in her ears), "What! that little squeaky thing?" The sparrow's song meant nothing to her at all, and how could she share the enthusiasm of the poet? Probably the warble of the robin, or the call of the meadowlark or of the highhole, if they chanced to hear them, meant no more to these girls. If we have no associations with these sounds, they will mean very little to us. Their merit as musical performances is very slight. It is as signs of joy and love in nature, as heralds of spring, and as the spirit of the woods and fields made audible, that they appeal to us. The drumming of the woodpeckers and of the ruffed grouse give great pleasure to a countryman, though these sounds have not the quality of real music. It is the same with the call of the migrating geese or the voice of any wild thing : our pleasure in them is entirely apart from any considerations of music. Why does the wild flower, as we chance upon it in the woods or bogs, give us more pleasure than the more elaborate flower of the garden or lawn? Because it comes as a surprise, offers a greater contrast with its surroundings, and suggests a spirit in wild nature that seems to take thought of itself and to aspire to beautiful forms.

The songs of caged birds are always disappointing, because such birds have nothing but their musical qualities to recommend them to us. We have separated them from that which gives quality and meaning to their songs. One recalls Emerson's lines : —

"I thought the sparrow's note from heaven,
    Singing at dawn on the alder bough;
I brought him home, in his nest, at even;
    He sings the song, but it cheers not now,
For I did not bring home the river and sky; —
    He sang to my ear, — they sang to my eye."

I have never yet seen a caged bird that I wanted, — at least, not on account of its song, — nor a wild flower that I wished to transfer to my garden. A caged skylark will sing its song sitting on a bit of turf in the bottom of the cage; but you want to stop your ears, it is so harsh and sibilant and penetrating. But up there against the morning sky, and above the wide expanse of fields, what delight we have in it! It is not the concord of sweet sounds: it is the soaring spirit of gladness and ecstasy raining down upon us from "heaven's gate."

Then, if to the time and the place one could only add the association, or hear the bird through the vista of the years, the song touched with the magic of youthful memories! One season a friend in England sent me a score of skylarks in a cage. I gave them their liberty in a field near my place. They drifted away, and I never heard them or saw them again. But one Sunday a Scotchman from a neighboring city called upon me, and declared with visible excitement that on his way along the road he had heard a skylark. He was not dreaming; he knew it was a skylark, though he had not heard one since he had left the banks of the Doon, a quarter of a century or more before. What pleasure it gave him! How much more the song meant to him than it would have meant to me! For the moment he was on his native heath again. Then I told him about the larks I had liberated, and he seemed to enjoy it all over again with renewed appreciation.

Many years ago some skylarks were liberated on Long Island, and they became established there, and may now occasionally be heard in certain localities.

One summer day a friend of mine was out there observing them; a lark was soaring and singing in the sky above him. An old Irishman came along, and suddenly stopped as if transfixed to the spot; a look of mingled delight and incredulity came into his face. Was he indeed hearing the bird of his youth? He took off his hat, turned his face skyward, and with moving lips and streaming eyes stood a long time regarding the bird. "Ah," my friend thought, "if I could only hear that song with his ears!" How it brought back his youth and all those long-gone days on his native hills!

The power of bird-songs over us is so much a matter of association that every traveler to other countries finds the feathered songsters of less merit than those he left behind. The stranger does not hear the birds in the same receptive, uncritical frame of mind as does the native; they are not in the same way the voices of the place and the season. What music can there be in that long, piercing, far-heard note of the first meadowlark in spring to any but a native, or in the "o-ka-lee" of the red-shouldered starling as he rests upon the willows in March? A stranger would probably recognize melody and a wild woodsy quality in the flutings of the veery thrush; but how much more they would mean to him after he had spent many successive Junes threading our northern trout-streams and encamping on their banks! The veery will come early in the morning, and again at sundown, and perch above your tent, and blow his soft, reverberant note for many minutes at a time. The strain repeats the echoes of the limpid stream in the halls and corridors of the leafy woods.

While in England in 1882, I rushed about two or three counties in late June and early July, bent on hearing the song of the nightingale, but missed it by a few days, and in some cases, as it seemed, only by a few hours. The nightingale seems to be wound up to go only so long, or till about the middle of June, and it is only by a rare chance that you hear one after that date. Then I came home to hear a nightingale in song one winter morning in a friend's house in the city. It was a curious let-down to my enthusiasm. A caged song in a city chamber in broad daylight, in lieu of the wild, free song in the gloaming of an English landscape! I closed my eyes, abstracted myself from my surroundings, and tried my best to fancy myself listening to the strain back there amid the scenes I had haunted about Haslemere and Godalming, but with poor success, I suspect. The nightingale's song, like the lark's, needs vista, needs all the accessories of time and place. The song is not all in the singing, any more than the wit is all in the saying. It is in the occasion, the surroundings, the spirit of which it is the expression. My friend said that the bird did not fully let itself out. Its song was a brilliant medley of notes, — no theme that I could detect, — like the lark's song in this respect; all the notes of the field and forest appeared to be the gift of this bird, but what tone! what accent! like that of a great poet!

Nearly every May I am seized with an impulse to go back to the scenes of my youth, and hear the bobolinks in the home meadows once more. I am sure they sing there better than anywhere else. They probably drink nothing but dew, and the dew distilled in those high pastoral regions has surprising virtues. It gives a clear, full, vibrant quality to the birds' voices that I have never heard elsewhere. The night of my arrival, I leave my southern window open, so that the meadow chorus may come pouring in before I am up in the morning. How it does transport me athwart the years, and make me a boy again, sheltered by the paternal wing! On one occasion, the third morning after my arrival, a bobolink appeared with a new note in his song. The note sounded like the word "baby" uttered with a peculiar, tender resonance: but it was clearly an interpolation; it did not belong there; it had no relation to the rest of the song. Yet the bird never failed to utter it with the same joy and confidence as the rest of his song. Maybe it was the beginning of a variation that will in time result in an entirely new bobolink song.

On my last spring visit to my native hills, my attention was attracted to another songster not seen or heard there in my youth, namely, the prairie horned lark. Flocks of these birds used to be seen in some of the Northern States in the late fall during their southern migrations; but within the last twenty years they have become regular summer residents in the hilly parts of many sections of New York and New England. They are genuine skylarks, and lack only the powers of song to make them as attractive as their famous cousins of Europe.

The larks are ground-birds when they perch, and sky-birds when they sing; from the turf to the clouds — nothing between. Our horned lark mounts upward on quivering wing in the true lark fashion, and, spread out against the sky at an altitude of two or three hundred feet, hovers and sings. The watcher and listener below holds him in his eye, but the ear catches only a faint, broken, half-inarticulate note now and then — mere splinters, as it were, of the song of the skylark. The song of the latter is continuous, and is loud and humming; it is a fountain of jubilant song up there in the sky: but our lark sings in snatches; at each repetition of its notes it dips forward and downward a few feet, and then rises again. One day I kept my eye upon one until it had repeated its song one hundred and three times; then it closed its wings, and dropped toward the earth like a plummet, as does its European congener. While I was watching the bird, a bobolink flew over my head, between me and the lark, and poured out his voluble and copious strain. "What a contrast," I thought, "between the voice of the spluttering, tongue-tied lark, and the free, liquid, and varied song of the bobolink!"

I have heard of a curious fact in the life-histories of these larks in the West. A Michigan woman once wrote me that her brother, who was an engineer on an express train that made daily trips between two Western cities, reported that many birds were struck by the engine every day, and killed — often as many as thirty on a trip of sixty miles. Birds of many kinds were killed, but the most common was a bird that went in flocks, the description of which answered to the horned lark. Since then I have read in a Minnesota newspaper that many horned larks are killed by railroad locomotives in that State. It was thought that the birds sat behind the rails to get out of the wind, and on starting up in front of the advancing train, were struck down by the engine. The Michigan engineer referred to thought that the birds gathered upon the track to earth their wings, or else to pick up the grain that leaks out of the wheat-trains, and sows the track from Dakota to the seaboard. Probably the wind which they might have to face in getting up was the prime cause of their being struck. One does not think of the locomotive as a bird-destroyer, though it is well known that many of the smaller mammals often fall beneath it.

BIRD-SONGS

A very interesting feature of our bird-songs is the wing-song, or song of ecstasy. It is not the gift of many of our birds. Indeed, less than a dozen species are known to me as ever singing on the wing. It seems to spring from more intense excitement and self-abandonment than the ordinary song delivered from the perch. When its joy reaches the point of rapture, the bird is literally carried off its feet, and up it goes into the air, pouring out its song as a rocket pours out its sparks. The skylark and the bobolink habitually do this, while a few others of our birds do it only on occasions. One summer, up in the Catskills, I added another name to my list of ecstatic singers — that of the vesper sparrow. Several times I heard a new song in the air, and caught a glimpse of the bird as it dropped back to the earth. My attention would be attracted by a succession of hurried, chirping notes, followed by a brief burst of song, then by the vanishing form of the bird. One day I was lucky enough to see the bird as it was rising to its climax in the air, and to identify it as the vesper sparrow. The burst of song that crowned the upward flight of seventy-five or one hundred feet was brief; but it was brilliant and striking, and entirely unlike the leisurely chant of the bird while upon the ground. It suggested a lark, but was less buzzing or humming. The preliminary chirping notes, uttered faster and faster as the bird mounted in the air, were like the trail of sparks which a rocket emits before its grand burst of color at the top of its flight.

It is interesting to note that this bird is quite lark-like in its color and markings, having the two lateral white quills in the tail, and it has the habit of elevating the feathers on the top of the head so as to suggest a crest. The solitary skylark that I discovered several years ago in a field near me was seen on several occasions paying his addresses to one of these birds, but the vesper-bird was shy, and eluded all his advances.

Probably the perch-songster among our ordinary birds that is most regularly seized with the fit of ecstasy that results in this lyric burst in the air, as I described in my first book, " Wake Robin," over thirty years ago, is the oven-bird, or wood-accentor — the golden-crowned thrush of the old ornithologists. Every loiterer about the woods knows this pretty, speckled-breasted, olive-backed little bird, which walks along over the dry leaves a few yards from him, moving its head as it walks, like a miniature domestic fowl. Most birds are very stiff-necked, like the robin, and as they run or hop upon the ground, carry the head as if it were riveted to the body. Not so the oven-bird, or the other birds that walk, as the cow-bunting, or the quail, or the crow. They move the head forward with the movement of the feet. The sharp, reiterated, almost screeching song of the oven-bird, as it perches on a limb a few feet from the ground, like the words, "preacher, preacher, preacher," or "teacher, teacher, teacher," uttered louder and louder, and repeated six or seven times, is also familiar to most ears; but its wild, ringing, rapturous burst of song in the air high above the tree-tops is not so well known. From a very prosy, tiresome, unmelodious singer, it is suddenly transformed for a brief moment into a lyric poet of great power. It is a great surprise. The bird undergoes a complete transformation. Ordinarily it is a very quiet, demure sort of bird. It walks about over the leaves, moving its head like a little hen; then perches on a limb a few feet from the ground and sends forth its shrill, rather prosy, unmusical chant. Surely it is an ordinary, commonplace bird. But wait till the inspiration of its flight-song is upon it. What a change! Up it goes through the branches of the trees, leaping from limb to limb, faster and faster, till it shoots from the tree-tops fifty or more feet into the air above them, and bursts into an ecstasy of song, rapid, ringing, lyrical; no more like its habitual performance than a match is like a rocket; brief but thrilling; emphatic but musical. Having reached its climax of flight and song, the bird closes its wings and drops nearly perpendicularly downward like the skylark. If its song were more prolonged, it would rival the song of that famous bird. The bird does this many times a day during early June, but oftenest at twilight. The song in quality and general cast is like that of its congener, the water-accentor, which, however, I believe is never delivered on the wing. From its habit of singing at twilight, and from the swift, darting motions of the bird, I am inclined to think that in it we have solved the mystery of Thoreau's "night-warbler," that puzzled and eluded him for years. Emerson told him he must beware of finding and booking it, lest life should have nothing more to show him. The older ornithologists must have heard this song many times, but they never seem to have suspected the identity of the singer.

Other birds that sing on the wing are the meadow-lark, goldfinch, purple finch, indigo-bird, Maryland yellow-throat, and woodcock. The flight-song of the woodcock I have heard but twice in my life. The first time was in the evening twilight about the middle of April. The bird was calling in the dusk "yeap, yeap," or "seap, seap," from the ground, —a peculiar reedy call. Then, by and by, it started upward on an easy slant, that peculiar whistling of its wings alone heard; then, at an altitude of one hundred feet or more, it began to float about in wide circles and broke out in an ecstatic chipper, almost a warble at times, with a peculiar smacking musical quality; then, in a minute or so, it dropped back to the ground again, not straight down like the lark, but more spirally, and continued its call as before. In less than five minutes it was up again. The

Woodcock on Nest

next time, a few years later, I heard the song in company with a friend, Dr. Clara Barrus. Let me give the woman's impression of the song as she afterward wrote it up for a popular journal.

"The sunset light was flooding all this May loveliness of field and farm and distant wood; song sparrows were blithely pouring out happiness by the throatful; peepers were piping and toads trilling, and we thought it no hardship to wait in such a place till the dusk should gather, and the wary woodcock announce his presence. But hark! while yet 'tis light, only a few rods distant, I hear that welcome 'seap . . . seap,' and lo! a chipper and a chirr, and past us he flies,—a direct, slanting upward flight, somewhat labored,—his bill showing long against the reddened sky. 'He has something in his mouth,' I start to say, when I bethink me what a long bill he has. Around, above us he flies in wide, ambitious circles, the while we are enveloped, as it were, in that hurried chippering sound—fine, elusive, now near, now distant. How rapid is the flight! Now it sounds faster and faster, 'like a whiplash flashed through the air,' said my friend; up, up he soars, till he becomes lost to sight at the instant that his song ends in that last mad ecstasy that just precedes his alighting."

The meadowlark sings in a level flight, half hovering in the air, giving voice to a rapid medley of lark-like notes. The goldfinch also sings in a level flight, beating the air slowly with its wings broadly open, and pouring out its jubilant, ecstatic strain I think it indulges in this wing-song only in the early season. After the mother bird has begun sitting, the male circles about within earshot of her, in that curious undulating flight, uttering his "per-chic-o-pee, per-chic-o-pee," while the female calls back to him in the tenderest tones, "Yes, lovie; I hear you." The indigo-bird and the purple finch, when their happiness becomes too full and buoyant for them longer to control it, launch into the air, and sing briefly, ecstatically, in a tremulous, hovering flight. The air-song of these birds does not differ essentially from the song delivered from the perch, except that it betrays more excitement, and hence is a more complete lyrical rapture.

The purple finch is our finest songster among the finches. Its strain is so soft and melodious, and touched with such a childlike gayety and plaintive-ness, that I think it might sound well even in a cage inside a room, if the bird would only sing with the same joyous abandonment, which, of course, it would not do.

It is not generally known that individual birds of the same species show different degrees of musical ability. This is often noticed in caged birds, among which the principle of variation seems more active; but an attentive observer notes the same fact in wild birds. Occasionally he hears one that in powers of song surpasses all its fellows. I have heard a sparrow, an oriole, and a wood thrush, each of which had a song of its own that far exceeded any other. I stood one day by a trout-stream, and suspended my fishing for several minutes to watch a song sparrow that was singing on a dry limb before me. He had five distinct songs, each as markedly different from the others as any human songs, which he repeated one after the other. He may have had a sixth or a seventh, but he bethought himself of some business in the next field, and flew away before he had exhausted his repertory. I once had a letter from Robert Louis Stevenson, who said he had read an account I had written of the song of the English blackbird. He said I might as well talk of the song of man; that every blackbird had its own song; and then he told me of a remarkable singer he used to hear somewhere amid the Scottish hills. But his singer was, of course, an exception ; twenty-four blackbirds out of every twenty-five probably sing the same song, with no appreciable variations: but the twenty-fifth may show extraordinary powers. I told Stevenson that his famous singer had probably been to school to some nightingale on the Continent or in southern England. I might have told him of the robin I once heard here that sang with great spirit and accuracy the song of the brown thrasher, or of another that had the note of the whip-poor-will interpolated in the regular robin song, or of still another that had the call of the quail. In each case the bird had probably heard the song and learned it while very young. In the Trossachs, in Scotland, I followed a song thrush about for a long time, attracted by its peculiar song. It repeated over and over again three or four notes of a well-known air, which it might have caught from some shepherd boy whistling to his flock or to his cow.

The songless birds — why has Nature denied them this gift? But they nearly all have some musical call or impulse that serves them very well. The quail has his whistle, the woodpecker his drum, the pewee his plaintive cry, the chickadee his exquisitely sweet call, the highhole his long, repeated "wick, wick, wick," one of the most welcome sounds of spring, the jay his musical gurgle, the hawk his scream, the crow his sturdy caw. Only one of our pretty birds of the orchard is reduced to an all but inaudible note, and that is the cedar-bird.

III

NATURE WITH CLOSED DOORS

DECEMBER in our climate is the month when Nature finally shuts up house and turns the key. She has been slowly packing up and putting away her things and closing a door and a window here and there all the fall. Now she completes the work and puts up the last bar. She is ready for winter. The leaves are all off the trees, except that here and there a beech or an oak or a hickory still clings to a remnant of its withered foliage. Her streams are full, her new growths of wood are ripened, her saps and juices are quiescent. The musk-rat has completed his house in the shallow pond or stream, the beaver in the northern woods has completed his. The wild mice and the chipmunk have laid up their winter stores of nuts and grains in their dens in the ground and in the cavities of trees. The woodchuck is rolled up in his burrow in the hillside, sleeping his long winter sleep. The coon has deserted his chamber in the old tree and gone into winter quarters in his den in the rocks. The winter birds have taken on a good coat of fat against the coming cold and a possible scarcity of food. The frogs and toads are all in their hibernaculums in the ground.

I saw it stated the other day, in a paper read before some scientific body, that the wood frogs retreat two feet into the ground beyond the reach of frost. In two instances I have found the wood frog in December with a covering of less than two inches of leaves and moss. It had buried itself in the soil and leaf mould only to the depth of the thickness of its own body, and for covering had only the ordinary coat of dry leaves and pine needles to be found in the wood. It was evidently counting upon the snow for its main protection. In one case I marked the spot, and returned there in early spring to see how the frog had wintered. I found it all right. Evidently it had some charm against the cold, for while the earth around and beneath it was yet frozen solid, there was no frost in the frog. It was not a brisk frog, but it was well, and when I came again on a warm day a week later, it had come forth from its retreat and was headed for the near-by marsh, where in April, with its kith and kin, it helped make the air vocal with its love-calls. A friend of mine, one mild day late in December, found a wood frog sitting upon the snow in the woods. She took it home and put it to bed in the soil of one of her flower-pots in the cellar. In the spring she found it in good condition, and in April carried it back to the woods. The hyla, or little piping frog, passes the winter in the ground like the wood frog. I have seen the toad go into the ground in the late fall. It is an interesting proceeding. It literally elbows its way into the soil. It sits on end, and works and presses with the sharp joints of its folded legs until it has sunk itself at a sufficient depth, which is only a few inches beneath the surface. The water frogs appear to pass the winter in the mud at the bottom of ponds and marshes. The queen bumblebee and the queen hornet, I think, seek out their winter quarters in holes in the ground in September, while the drones and the workers perish. The honey-bees do not hibernate: they must have food all winter; but our native wild bees are dormant during the cold months, and survive the winter only in the person of the queen mother. In the spring these queens set up housekeeping alone, and found new families.

Insects in all stages of their growth are creatures of the warmth; the heat is the motive power that makes them go; when this fails, they are still. The katydids rasp away in the fall as long as there is warmth enough to keep them going; as the heat fails, they fail, till from the emphatic " Katy did it " of August they dwindle to a hoarse, dying, " Kate, Kate," in October. Think of the stillness that falls upon the myriad wood-borers in the dry trees and stumps in the forest as the chill of autumn comes on. All summer have they worked incessantly in oak and hickory and birch and chestnut and spruce, some of them making a sound exactly like that of the old-fashioned hand augur, others a fine, snapping, and splintering sound; but as the cold comes on, they go slower and slower, till they finally cease to move. A warm day starts them again, slowly or briskly according to the degree of heat, but in December they are finally stilled for the season. These creatures, like the big fat grubs of the June beetles which one sometimes finds in the ground or in decayed wood, are full of frost in winter; cut one of the big grubs in two, and it looks like a lump of ice cream.

Some time in October the crows begin to collect together in large flocks and establish their winter quarters. They choose some secluded wood for a roosting-place, and thither all the crows for many square miles of country betake themselves at night, and thence they disperse in all directions again in the early morning. The crow is a social bird, a true American; no hermit or recluse is he. The winter probably brings them together in these large colonies for purposes of sociability and for greater warmth. By roosting close together and quite filling a treetop, there must result some economy of heat.

I have seen it stated in a rhetorical flight of some writer that the new buds crowd the old leaves off. But this is not true as a rule. The new bud is formed in the axil of the old leaf long before the leaves are ready to fall. With only two species of our trees known to me might the swelling bud push off the old leaf. In the sumach and button-ball or plane-tree the new bud is formed immediately under the base of the old leaf-stalk, by which it is covered like a cap. Examine the fallen leaves of these trees, and you will see the cavity in the base of each where the new bud was cradled. Why the beech, the oak, and the hickory cling to their old leaves is not clear. It may be simply a slovenly trait — inability to finish and have done with a thing — a fault of so many people. Some oaks and beeches appear to lack decision of character. It requires strength and vitality, it seems, simply to let go. Kill a tree suddenly, and the leaves wither upon the branches. How neatly and thoroughly the maples, the ashes, the birches, the elm clean up. They are tidy, energetic trees, and can turn over a new leaf without hesitation.

A correspondent, writing to me from one of the colleges, suggests that our spring really begins in December, because the "annual cycle of vegetable life" seems to start then. At this time he finds that many of our wild flowers — the bloodroot, hepatica, columbine, shinleaf, maidenhair fern, etc. — have all made quite a start toward the next season's growth, in some cases the new shoot being an inch high. But the real start of the next season's vegetable life in this sense is long before December. It is in late summer, when the new buds are formed on the trees. Nature looks ahead, and makes ready for the new season in the midst of the old. Cut open the terminal hickory buds in the late fall and you will find the new growth of the coming season all snugly packed away there, many times folded up and wrapped about by protecting scales. The catkins of the birches, alders, and hazel are fully formed, and as in the case of the buds, are like eggs to be hatched by the warmth of spring. The present season is always the mother of the next, and the inception takes place long before the sun loses his power. The eggs that hold the coming crop of insect life are mostly laid in the late summer or early fall, and an analogous start is made in the vegetable world. The egg, the seed, the bud, are all alike in many ways, and look to the future. Our earliest spring flower, the skunk-cabbage, may be found with its round green spear-point an inch or two above the mould in December. It is ready to welcome and make the most of the first fitful March warmth. Look at the elms, too, and see how they swarm with buds. In early April they suggest a swarm of bees.

In all cases, before Nature closes her house in the fall, she makes ready for its spring opening.

IV

THE WIT OF A DUCK

THE homing instinct in birds and animals is one of their most remarkable traits: their strong local attachments and their skill in finding their way back when removed to a distance. It seems at times as if they possessed some extra sense — the home sense — which operates unerringly. I saw this illustrated one spring in the case of a mallard drake.

My son had two ducks, and to mate with them he procured a drake of a neighbor who lived two miles south of us. He brought the drake home in a bag. The bird had no opportunity to see the road along which it was carried, or to get the general direction, except at the time of starting, when the boy carried him a few rods openly.

He was placed with the ducks in a spring run, under a tree in a secluded place on the river slope, about a hundred yards from the highway. The two ducks treated him very contemptuously. It was easy to see that the drake was homesick from the first hour, and he soon left the presence of the scornful ducks.

Then we shut the three in the barn together,

and kept them there a day and a night. Still the friendship did not ripen; the ducks and the drake separated the moment we let them out. Left to himself, the drake at once turned his head homeward, and started up the hill for the highway.

Then we shut the trio up together again for a couple of days, but with the same results as before. There seemed to be but one thought in the mind of the drake, and that was home.

Several times we headed him off and brought him back, till finally on the third or fourth day I said to my son, "If that drake is really bound to go home, he shall have an opportunity to make the trial, and I will go with him to see that he has fair play." We withdrew, and the homesick mallard started up through the currant patch, then through the vineyard toward the highway which he had never seen.

When he reached the fence, he followed it south till he came to the open gate, where he took to the road as confidently as if he knew for a certainty that it would lead him straight to his mate. How eagerly he paddled along, glancing right and left, and increasing his speed at every step! I kept about fifty yards behind him. Presently he met a dog; he paused and eyed the animal for a moment, and then turned to the right along a road which diverged just at that point, and which led to the railroad station. I followed, thinking the drake would soon lose his bearings, and get hopelessly confused in the tangle of roads that converged at the station.

But he seemed to have an exact map of the country in his mind; he soon left the station road, went around a house, through a vineyard, till he struck a stone fence that crossed his course at right angles; this he followed eastward till it was joined by a barbed wire fence, under which he passed and again entered the highway he had first taken. Then down the road he paddled with renewed confidence: under the trees, down a hill, through a grove, over a bridge, up the hill again toward home.

Presently he found his clue cut in two by the railroad track; this was something he had never before seen; he paused, glanced up it, then down it, then at the highway across it, and quickly concluded this last was his course. On he went again, faster and faster.

He had now gone half the distance, and was getting tired. A little pool of water by the roadside caught his eye. Into it he plunged, bathed, drank, preened his plumage for a few moments, and then started homeward again. He knew his home was on the upper side of the road, for he kept his eye bent in that direction, scanning the fields. Twice he stopped, stretched himself up, and scanned the landscape intently; then on again. It seemed as if an invisible cord was attached to him, and he was being pulled down the road.

Just opposite a farm lane which led up to a group of farm buildings, and which did indeed look like his home lane, he paused and seemed to be debating with himself. Two women just then came along; they lifted and flirted their skirts, for it was raining, and this disturbed him again and decided him to take to the farm lane. Up the lane he went, rather doubtingly, I thought.

In a few moments it brought him into a barn-yard, where a group of hens caught his eye. Evidently he was on good terms with hens at home, for he made up to these eagerly as if to tell them his troubles; but the hens knew not ducks; they withdrew suspiciously, then assumed a threatening attitude, till one old " dominic " put up her feathers and charged upon him viciously.

Again he tried to make up to them, quacking softly, and again he was repulsed. Then the cattle in the yard spied this strange creature and came sniffing toward it, full of curiosity.

The drake quickly concluded he had got into the wrong place, and turned his face southward again. Through the fence he went into a plowed field. Presently another stone fence crossed his path; along this he again turned toward the highway. In a few minutes he found himself in a corner formed by the meeting of two stone fences. Then he turned appealingly to me, uttering the soft note of the mallard. To use his wings never seemed to cross his mind.

THE WIT OF A DUCK

Well, I am bound to confess that I helped the drake over the wall, but I sat him down in the road as impartially as I could. How well his pink feet knew the course! How they flew up the road! His green head and white throat fairly twinkled under the long avenue of oaks and chestnuts.

At last we came in sight of the home lane, which led up to the farmhouse one hundred or more yards from the road. I was curious to see if he would recognize the place. At the gate leading into the lane he paused. He had just gone up a lane that looked like that and had been disappointed. What should he do now? Truth compels me to say that he overshot the mark: he kept on hesitatingly along the highway.

It was now nearly night. I felt sure the duck would soon discover his mistake, but I had not time to watch the experiment further. I went around the drake and turned him back. As he neared the lane this time he seemed suddenly to see some familiar landmark, and he rushed up it at the top of his speed. His joy and eagerness were almost pathetic.

I followed close. Into the house yard he rushed with uplifted wings, and fell down almost exhausted by the side of his mate. A half hour later the two were nipping the grass together in the pasture, and he, I have no doubt, was eagerly telling her the story of his adventures.

V

FACTORS IN ANIMAL LIFE

THE question that the Californian schoolchildren put to me, "Have the birds got sense?" still "sticks in my crop."

Such extraordinary sense has been attributed to most of the wild creatures by several of our latter day nature-writers, that I have been moved to examine the whole question more thoroughly than ever before, and to find out, as far as I can, just how much and what kind of sense the birds and four-footed beasts have.

In this and in some following chapters I shall make an effort to use my own sense to the best advantage in probing that of the animals, which has, as I think, been so vastly overrated.

When sentiment gets overripe, it becomes sentimentalism. The sentiment for nature which has been so assiduously cultivated in our times is fast undergoing this change, and is softening into sentimentalism toward the lower animals. Many a wholesome feeling can be pushed so far that it becomes a weakness and a sign of disease. Pity for the sufferings of our brute neighbors may be a manly feeling; and then again it may be so fostered and cosseted that it becomes maudlin and unworthy. When hospitals are founded for sick or homeless cats and dogs, when all forms of vivisection are cried down, when the animals are humanized and books are written to show that the wild creatures have schools and kindergartens, and that their young are instructed and disciplined in quite the human way by their fond parents; when we want to believe that reason and not instinct guides them, that they are quite up in some of the simpler arts of surgery, mending or amputating their own broken limbs and salving their wounds, — when, I say, our attitude toward the natural life about us and our feeling for it have reached the stage implied by these things, then has sentiment degenerated into sentimentalism, and our appreciation of nature lost its firm edge.

No doubt there is a considerable number of people in any community that are greatly taken with this improved anthropomorphic view of wild nature now current among us. Such a view tickles the fancy and touches the emotions. It makes the wild creatures so much more interesting. Shall we deny anything to a bird or beast that makes it more interesting, and more worthy of our study and admiration?

This sentimental view of animal life has its good side and its bad side. Its good side is its result in making us more considerate and merciful toward our brute neighbors; its bad side is seen in the degree to which it leads to a false interpretation of their lives. The tendency to which I refer is no doubt partly the result of our growing humanitarianism and feeling of kinship with all the lower orders of creation, and partly due to the fact that we live in a time of impromptu nature study, when birds and plants and trees are fast becoming a fad with half the population, and when the "yellow" reporter is abroad in the fields and woods. Never before in my time have so many exaggerations and misconceptions of the wild life about us been current in the popular mind. It is becoming the fashion to ascribe to the lower animals nearly all our human motives and attributes, and often to credit them with plans and devices that imply reason and a fair amount of mechanical knowledge. An illustration of this is the account of the nest of a pair of orioles, as described in the "North American Review" for May, 1903, by a writer of popular nature books. These orioles built a nest so extraordinary that it can be accounted for only on the theory that there *is* a school of the woods, and that these two birds had been pupils there and had taken an advanced course in Strings. Among other things impossible for birds to do, these orioles tied a knot in the end of a string to prevent its fraying in the wind! If the whole idea were not too preposterous for even a half-witted child to believe, one might ask, What in the name of anything and every-thing but the " Modern School of Nature Study " do orioles know about strings fraying in the wind and the use of knots to prevent it ? They have never had occasion to know; they have had no experience with strings that hang loose and unravel in the wind. They often use strings, to be sure, in building their nests, but they use them in a sort of haphazard way, weaving them awkwardly into the structure, and leaving no loose ends that would suffer by fraying in the wind. Sometimes they use strings in attaching the nest to the limb, but they never knot or tie them; they simply wind them round and round as a child might. It is possible that a bird might be taught to tie a knot with its foot and beak, though I should have to see it done to be convinced. But the orioles in question not only tied knots; they tied them with a " reversed double hitch, the kind that a man uses in cinching his saddle"! More wonderful still, not finding in a New England elm-embowered town a suitable branch from which to suspend their nest, the birds went down upon the ground and tied three twigs together in the form of "a perfectly measured triangle" (no doubt working from a plan drawn to a scale). They attached to the three sides of this frame-work four strings of equal length (eight or ten inches), all carefully doubled, tied them to a heavier string, carried the whole ingenious contrivance to a tree, and tied it fast to a limb in precisely the way you or I would have done it! From this framework they suspended their nest, the whole structure being about two feet long, and having the effect of a small hanging basket. Still more astonishing, when the genuineness of the nest is questioned, a man is found who makes affidavit that he saw the orioles build it! After such a proceeding, how long will it be before the water-birds are building little rush cradles for their young, or rush boats to be driven about the ponds and lakes by means of leaf sails, or before Jenny Wren will be living in a log cabin of her own construction? How long will it be before some one makes affidavit that the sparrow with his bow and arrow has actually been seen to kill Cock Robin, and the beetle with his thread and needle engaged in making the shroud? Birds show the taste and skill of their kind in building their nests, but rarely any individual ingenuity and inventiveness. The nest referred to is on a plane entirely outside of Nature and her processes. It belongs to a different order of things, the order of mechanical contrivances, and was of course "made up," probably from a real oriole's nest, and the writer who vouches for its genuineness has been the victim of a clever practical joke — a willing victim, no doubt, since he is looking in Nature for just this kind of thing, and since he believes there is "absolutely no limit to the variety and adaptiveness of Nature even in a single species." If there is no such limit, then I suppose we need not be surprised to meet a winged horse, or a centaur, or a mermaid at any time.

It is as plain as anything can be that the animals share our emotional nature in vastly greater measure than they do our intellectual or our moral nature; and because they do this, because they show fear, love, joy, anger, sympathy, jealousy, because they suffer and are glad, because they form friendships and local attachments and have the home and paternal instincts, in short, because their lives run parallel to our own in so many particulars, we come, if we are not careful, to ascribe to them the whole human psychology. But it is equally plain that of what we mean by mind, intellect, they show only a trace now and then. They do not accumulate a store of knowledge any more than they do a store of riches. A store of knowledge is impossible without language. Man began to emerge from the lower orders when he invented a language of some sort. As the language of animals is little more than various cries expressive of pleasure or pain, or fear or suspicion, they do not think in any proper sense, because they have no terms in which to think — no language. I shall have more to say upon this point in another chapter. One trait they do show which is the first step toward knowledge — curiosity. Nearly all the animals show at times varying degrees of curiosity, but here again an instinctive feeling of possible danger probably lies back of it. They even that has not yet been fully settled. That imitation has much to do with it admits of little doubt. The song of a bird is of secondary importance in its life. Birds reared in captivity, where they have never heard the songs of their kind, sing at the proper age, but not always the songs of their parents. Mr. Scott of Princeton proved this with his orioles. They sang at the proper age, but not the regular oriole song. I am told that there is a well-authenticated case of an English sparrow brought up with canaries that learned to sing like a canary. "The Hon. Daines Barrington placed three young linnets with three different foster-parents, the skylark, the woodlark, and the titlark or meadow-pipit, and each adopted, through imitation, the song of its foster-parent." I have myself heard goldfinches that were reared in a cage sing beautifully, but not the regular goldfinch song; it was clearly the song of a finch, but of what finch I could not have told. I have also heard a robin that sang to perfection the song of the brown thrasher; it had, no doubt, caught it by imitation. I have heard another robin that had the call of the quail interpolated into its own proper robin's song. But I have yet to hear of a robin building a nest like a brown thrasher, or of an oriole building a nest like a robin, or of kingfishers drilling for grubs in a tree. The hen cannot keep out of the water the ducks she has hatched, nor can the duck coax into the water the chickens she has hatched. The cowbird hatched

seem to show at times a kind of altruistic feeling. A correspondent writes me that she possessed a canary which lived to so great an age that it finally became so feeble it could not crack the seeds she gave it, when the other birds, its own progeny, it is true, fed it; and Darwin cites cases of blind birds, in a state of nature, being fed by their fellows. Probably it would be hasty to conclude that such acts show anything more than instinct. I should be slow to ascribe to the animals any notion of the uses of punishment as we practice it, though the cat will box her kittens when they play too long with her tail, and the mother hen will separate her chickens when they get into a fight, and sometimes peck one or both of them on the head, as much as to say, "There, don't you do that again." The rooster will in the same way separate two hens when they are fighting. On the surface this seems like a very human act, but can we say that it is punishment or discipline in the human sense, as having for its aim a betterment of the manners of the kittens or of the chickens? The cat aims to get rid of an annoyance, and the rooster and the mother hen interfere to prevent an injury to members of their family; they exhibit the paternal and maternal instinct of protection. More than that would imply ethical considerations, of which the lower animals are not capable. The act of the baboon, mentioned by Darwin, I believe, that examined the paws of the cat that had scratched it, and then deliberately bit off the nails, belongs to a different and to a higher order of conduct.

A complete statement of the factors that shape the lives of the lower orders would include three terms — instinct, imitation (though, doubtless, this is instinctive), and experience. Instinct is, of course, the main factor, and by this term we mean that which prompts an animal or a man to act spontaneously, without instruction or experience. All creatures are imitative, and man himself not the least so. I had a visit the other day from a woman who had spent the last two years in London, and her speech betrayed the fact; she had quite unconsciously caught certain of the English mannerisms of speech. A few years in the South will give the New Englander the Southern accent, and vice versa. The young are, of course, more imitative than the old. Children imitate their parents; the young writer imitates his favorite author.

Animals of different species closely associated will imitate each other. A lady writes me that she has a rabbit that lives in a cage with a monkey, and that it has caught many of the monkey's ways. I can well believe it. Dogs reared with cats have been known to acquire the cat habit of licking the paws and then washing the ears and face. Wolves reared with dogs learn to bark, and who has not seen a dog draw its face as if trying to laugh as its master does? When a cat has been taught to sit up for its food,

its kittens have been known to imitate the mother. Darwin tells of a cat that used to put its paw into the mouth of a narrow milk-jug and then lick it off, and that its kittens soon learned the same trick. In all such cases, hasty observers say the mother taught its young. Certainly the young learned, but there was no effort to teach on the part of the parent. Unconscious imitation did it all. Our "Modern School of Nature Study" would say that the old sow teaches her pigs to root when they follow her afield, rooting in their little ways as she does. But would she not root if she had no pigs, and would not the pigs root if they had no mother? All acts necessary to an animal's life and to the continuance of the species are instinctive; the creature does not have to be taught them, nor are they acquired by imitation. The bird does not have to be taught to build its nest or to nor the beaver to build its dam or its house, nor otter or the seal to swim, nor the young of mamm to suckle, nor the spider to spin its web, nor the to weave its cocoon. Nature does not trust things to chance; they are too vital. The thing an animal acquires by imitation are of second portance in its life. As soon as the calf, or th or the colt can get upon its feet, its first imp find the udder of its dam. It requires no i or experience to take this important step

How far the different species of song-bi each their peculiar songs by imitation i

and reared by the sparrow, or the warbler, or the vireo does not sing the song of the foster-parent. Why? Did its parent not try to teach it? I have no evidence that young birds sing, except occasionally in a low, tentative kind of way, till they return the following season, and then birds of a feather flock together, robins staying with robins, and cowbirds with cowbirds, each singing the song of its species. The songs of bobolinks differ in different localities, but those of the same locality always sing alike. I once had a caged skylark that imitated the songs of nearly every bird in my neighborhood.

Mr. Leander S. Keyser, author of "Birds of the Rockies," relates in "Forest and Stream" the results of his experiments with a variety of birds taken from the nest while very young and reared in captivity; among them meadowlarks, red-winged blackbirds, brown thrashers, blue jays, wood thrushes, catbirds, flickers, woodpeckers, and several others. Did they receive any parental instruction? Not a bit of it, and yet at the proper age they flew, perched, called, and sang like their wild fellows — all except the robins and the red-winged blackbirds: these did not sing the songs of their species, but sang a medley made up of curious imitations of human and other sounds. And the blue jay never learned to sing "the sweet gurgling roulade of the wild jays," though it gave the blue jay call correctly. Mr. Keyser's experiment was interesting and valuable, but his sagacity fails him when interpreting the action of the jay in roosting in an exposed place after it had been given its liberty. He thinks this showed how little instinct can be relied on, and how much the bird needed parental instruction. Could he not see that the artificial life of the bird in the cage had demoralized its instincts, and that acquired habits had supplanted native tendencies? The bird had learned to be unafraid in the cage, and why should it be afraid out of the cage? This reminds me of a letter from a correspondent: he had a tame crow that was not afraid of a gun; therefore he concluded that the old crows must instill the fear of guns into their young! Why should the crow be afraid of a gun, if it had learned not to be afraid of the gunner?

I have seen a young chickadee fly late in the day from the nest in the cavity of a tree straight to a pear-tree, where it perched close to the trunk and remained unregarded by its parents till next morning. But no doubt its parents had given it minute directions before it left the nest how to fly and where to perch!

That animals learn by experience in a limited way is very certain. Yet that old birds build better nests or sing better than young ones it would be hard to prove, though it seems reasonable that it should be so.

Rarely does one see nests of the same species of

varying degrees of excellence — that is, first nests in the spring. The second nest of any species is likely to be a more hurried and incomplete affair. Some species are at all times poor nest-builders, as the cuckoos and the pigeons. Other birds are good nest-builders, as the orioles, the thrushes, the finches, the warblers, the hummingbirds, and one never finds an inferior specimen of the nests of any of these birds. There is probably no more improvement in this respect among birds than there is among insects.

I have no proof that wild birds improve in singing. One does not hear a vireo, or a finch, or a thrush, or a warbler that is noticeably inferior as a songster to its fellows; their songs are all alike, except in the few rare cases when one hears a master songster among its kind; but whether this mastery is natural or acquired, who shall tell?

What birds learn about migration, if anything, I do not see that we have any means of finding out.

It has been observed of birds reared under artificial conditions that the young males practice a long time before they sing well. That this is true of wild birds, there is no proof. What birds and animals learn by experience is greater cunning. Does not even an old trout know more about hooks than a young one? Birds of any kind that are much hunted become wilder, even though they have not had the experience of being shot. Ask any duck or grouse or quail hunter if this is not so. Our ruffed grouse learns to fly with a corkscrew motion where it is much fired at on the wing. How wary and cautious the fox becomes in regions where it is much trapped and hunted! Even the woodchuck becomes very wild on the farms where it is much shot at, and this wildness extends to its young. In his "Wilderness Hunter" President Roosevelt says the same thing of the big game of the Rockies. Antelope and deer can be lured near the concealed hunter by the waving of a small flag till they are shot at a few times. Then they see through the trick. "The burnt child fears the fire." Animals profit by experience in this way; they learn what not to do. In the accumulation of positive knowledge, so far as we know, they make little or no progress. Birds and beasts will adapt themselves more or less to their environment, but plants and trees will do that, too. The rats in Jamaica have learned to nest in trees to escape the mongoose, but this is only the triumph of the instinct of self-preservation. The mongoose has not yet learned to climb trees; the pressure of need is not yet great enough. It is said that in districts subject to floods moor-hens often build in trees. All animals will change their habits under pressure of necessity; man changes his without this pressure. The Duke of Argyll saw a bald eagle seize a fish in the stream — an unusual proceeding; but the eagle was doubtless very hungry, and there was no osprey near upon whom to levy tribute.

Romanes found that rats would get certain semi-liquid foods out of a bottle with their tails, as a cat will get milk out of a jar with her paw, but neither ever progresses so far as to use any sort of tool for the purpose, or to tip the vessel over. Animals practice concealment to secure their prey, but not deception, as man does. They do not use lures or disguises, or traps or poison.

There is, of course, no limit to the variety and adaptiveness of nature taken as a whole, but each species is hedged about by impassable limitations. The ouzel is akin to the thrushes, and yet it lives along and in the water. Does it ever take to the fields and woods, and live on fruit and land-insects, and nest in trees like other thrushes? So with all birds and beasts. They vary constantly, but not in one lifetime, and the sum of these variations, accumulated through natural selection, as Darwin has shown, gives rise, in the course of long periods of time, to new species.

As I have already said, domestic animals vary more than wild ones. Every farmer and poultry-grower knows that some hens are better with chickens than others — more motherly, more careful — and rear a greater number of their brood. The same is true of sows with pigs. Some sows will eat their pigs, and wild animals in cages often destroy their young. Some ewes will not own their lambs, and occasionally a cow will not own her calf. (Such cases

show perverted or demoralized instinct.) Similar
to these are the strange friendships that sometimes
occur among the domestic animals, as that of a sheep
with a cow, a goose with a horse, or a hen adopting
kittens. In a state of nature these curious attachments probably never spring up. Instinct is likely to
be more or less demoralized when animal life touches
human life.

With the wild creatures we sometimes see one
instinct overcoming another, as when fear drives
a bird to desert its nest, or when the instinct of migration leads a pair of swallows to desert their
unfledged young.

A great many young birds come to grief by leaving
the nest before they can fly. In such cases, I suppose, they disobey the parental instructions! I find it
easier to believe that instinct is at fault, or that one
instinct has overcome another; something has disturbed or alarmed the young birds, and the fear of
danger has led them to attempt flight before their
wings were strong enough. Once, when I was climbing up to the nest of a broad-winged hawk, the
young took fright and launched out in the air, coming to the ground only a few rods away.

Instinct, natural prompting, is the main matter,
after all. It makes up at least nine tenths of the
lives of all our wild neighbors. How much has fear
had to do in shaping their lives and in perpetuating
them! And "fear of any particular enemy," says

Darwin, "is certainly an instinctive quality." It has been said that kittens confined in a box, and which have never known a dog, will spit and put up their backs at a hand that has just stroked a dog, — even before their eyes are opened, one authority says, but this I doubt. My son's tame gray squirrel had never seen chestnuts, nor learned about them in the school of the woods, and yet when he was offered some, he fairly danced with excitement; he put his paws eagerly around them and drew them to him, and chattered, and looked threateningly at all about him. Does man know his proper food in the same way? The child has only the instinct to eat, and will put anything into its mouth.

How the instinctive wildness of the turkey crops out in the young! Let the mother turkey while hovering her brood give the danger-signal, and the young will run from under her and hide in the grass. Why? To give her a chance to fly and decoy away the enemy. I think young chickens will do the same. Young partridges hatched under a hen run away at once. Pheasants in England reared under a domestic fowl are as wild as in a state of nature. Some California quail hatched under a bantam hen in the Zoo in New York did not heed the calls of their foster-mother at all the first week, but at her alarm-note they instantly squatted, showing that the danger-cry of a fowl is a kind of universal language that all species understand. One may prove this at any time by arousing the fears of any wild bird: how all the other birds catch the alarm! Charles St. John says that in Scotland the stag you are stalking is sure to be put to flight if it hears the alarm-cry of the cock-grouse. You see it is more important that the wild creatures should understand the danger-signals of one another than that they should understand the rest of their language.

To what extent animals reason, or show any glimmering of what we call reason, is a much-debated question among animal psychologists, and I shall have more to say upon the subject later on. Dogs undoubtedly show gleams of reason, and other animals in domestication, such as the elephant and the monkey. One does not often feel like questioning Darwin's conclusions, yet the incident of the caged bear which he quotes, that pawed the water in front of its cage to create a current that should float within its reach a piece of bread that had been placed there, does not, in my judgment, show any reasoning about the laws of hydrostatics. The bear would doubtless have pawed a cloth in the same way, vaguely seeking to draw the bread within reach. But when an elephant blows through his trunk upon the ground *beyond* an object which he wants, but which is beyond his reach, so that the rebounding air will drive it toward him, he shows something very much like reason.

Instinct is a kind of natural reason, — reason

that acts without proof or experience. The principle of life in organic nature seeks in all ways to express and to perpetuate itself. It finds many degrees of expression and fulfillment in the vegetable world; it finds higher degrees of expression and fulfillment in the animal world, reaching its highest development in man.

That the animals, except those that have been long associated with man, and they only in occasional gleams and hints, are capable of any of our complex mental processes, that they are capable of an act of reflection, of connecting cause and effect, of putting this and that together, is to me void of proof. Why, there are yet savage tribes in which the woman is regarded as the sole parent of the child. When the mother is sick at childbirth, the father takes to his bed and feigns the illness he does not feel, in order to establish his relationship to the child. It is not at all probable that the males of any species of animals, or the females either, are guided or influenced in their actions by the desire for offspring, or that they possess anything like knowledge of the connection between their love-making and their offspring. This knowledge comes of reflection, and reflection the lower animals are not capable of. But I shall have more to say upon this point in another chapter, entitled "What do Animals Know?" I will only say here that animals are almost as much under the dominion of absolute nature, or what we call instinct, innate tendency, habit of growth, as are the plants and trees. Their lives revolve around three wants or needs — the want of food, of safety, and of offspring. It is in securing these ends that all their wit is developed. They have no wants outside of these spheres, as man has. Their social wants and their love of beauty, as in some of the birds, are secondary. It is quite certain that the animals that store up food for the winter do not take any thought of the future. Nature takes thought for them and gives them their provident instinct. The jay, by his propensity to carry away and hide things, plants many of our oak and chestnut trees, but who dares say that he does this on purpose, any more than that the insects cross-fertilize the flowers on purpose? Sheep do not take thought of the wool upon their backs that is to protect them from the cold of winter, nor does the fox of his fur. In the tropics sheep cease to grow wool in three or four years.

All the lower animals, so far as I know, swim the first time they find themselves in the water. They do not have to be taught: it is a matter of instinct. It is what we should expect from our knowledge of their lives. Not so with man; he must learn to swim as he learns so many other things. The stimulus of the water does not at once set in motion his legs and arms in the right way, as it does the animal's legs ; his powers of reason and reflection paralyze him — his brain carries him down

Not until he has learned to resign himself to the water as the animal does, and to go on all fours, can he swim. As soon as the boy ceases to struggle against his tendency to sink, assumes the horizontal position, and strikes out as the animal does, with but one thought, and that to apply his powers of locomotion to the medium about him, he swims as a matter of course. It is said that children have sometimes been known to swim when thrown into the water. Their animal instincts were not thwarted by their powers of reflection. Doubtless this never happened to a grown person. Moreover, is it not probable that the specific gravity of the hairless human body is greater than that of the hair-covered animal, and that it sinks, while that of the cat or dog floats? This, with the erect position of man, makes swimming with him an art that must be acquired.

There is no better illustration of the action of instinct as opposed to conscious intelligence than is afforded by the parasitic birds, — the cuckoo in Europe and the cowbird in this country, — birds that lay their eggs in the nests of other birds. Darwin speculates as to how this instinct came about, but whatever may have been its genesis, it is now a fixed habit among these birds. Moreover, the instinct of the blind young alien, a day or two after it is hatched, to throw or crowd its foster-brothers out of the nest is a strange and anomalous act, and is as untaught and unreasoned as anything in vegetable life. But when our yellow warbler, finding this strange egg of the cowbird in her nest, proceeds to bury it by putting another bottom in the nest and carrying up the sides to correspond, she shows something very much like sense and judgment, though of a clumsy kind. How much simpler and easier it would be to throw out the strange egg! I have known the cowbird herself to carry an egg from a nest in which she wished to deposit one of her own. Again, how stupid and ludicrous it seems on the part of the mother sparrow, or warbler, or vireo, when she goes about toiling desperately to satisfy the hunger of her big clamorous bantling of a cowbird, never suspecting that she has been imposed upon!

Of course the line that divides man from the lower orders is not a straight line. It has many breaks and curves and deep indentations. The man-like apes, as it were, mark where the line rises up into the domain of man. Furthermore, the elephant and the dog, especially as we know them in domestication, encroach upon man's territory.

Men are born with aptitudes for different things, but the art and the science of them all they have to learn; proficiency comes with practice. Man must learn to spin his web, to build his house, to sing his song, to know his food, to sail his craft, to find his way — things that the animals know " from the jump." The animal inherits its knowledge and its skill: man must acquire his by individual effort; all he inherits is capacity in varying degrees for these things. The animal does rational things without an exercise of reason. It is intelligent as nature is intelligent. It does not know that it knows, or how it knows, while man does. Man's knowledge is the light of his mind that shines on many and widely different objects, while the knowledge of animals cannot be symbolized by the term "light" at all. The animal acts blindly so far as any conscious individual illumination or act of judgment is concerned. It does the thing unwittingly, because it must. Confront it with a new condition, and it has no resources to meet that condition. The animal knows what necessity taught its progenitors, and it knows that only as a spontaneous impulse to do certain things.

Instinct, I say, is a great matter, and often shames reason. It adapts means to an end, it makes few or no mistakes, it takes note of times and seasons, it delves, it bores, it spins, it weaves, it sews, it builds, it makes paper, it constructs a shelter, it navigates the air and the water, it is provident and thrifty, it knows its enemies, it outwits its foes, it crosses oceans and continents without compass, it foreshadows nearly all the arts and trades and occupations of mankind, it is skilled without practice, and wise without experience. How it arose, what its genesis was, who can tell? Probably natural selection has been the chief agent in its development. If natural selection has developed and sharpened the claws of the cat and the scent of the fox, why should it not develop and sharpen their wits also? The remote ancestors of the fox or of the crow were doubtless less shrewd and cunning than the crows and the foxes of to-day. The instinctive intelligence of an animal of our time is the sum of the variations toward greater intelligence of all its ancestors. What man stores in language and in books — the accumulated results of experience — the animals seem to have stored in instinct. As Darwin says, a man cannot, on his first trial, make a stone hatchet or a canoe through his power of imitation. "He has to learn his work by practice; a beaver, on the other hand, can make its dam or canal, and a bird its nest, as well or nearly as well, and a spider its wonderful web quite as well, the first time it tries as when old and experienced."

An animal shows intelligence, as distinct from instinct, when it takes advantage of any circumstance that arises at the moment, when it finds new ways, whether better or not, as when certain birds desert their old nesting-sites, and take up with new ones afforded by man. This act, at least, shows power of choice. The birds and beasts all quickly avail themselves of any new source of food supply. Their wits are probably more keen and active here than in any other direction. It is said that in Oklahoma the coyotes have learned to tell ripe watermelons from unripe ones by scratching upon them.

If they have not, they probably will. Eating is the one thing that engrosses the attention of all creatures, and the procuring of food has been a great means of education to all.

I notice that certain of the wood-folk — mice and squirrels and birds — eat mushrooms. If I would eat them, I must learn how to distinguish the edible from the poisonous ones. I have no special sense to guide me in the matter, as doubtless the squirrels have. Their instinct is sure where my reason fails. It would be very interesting to know if they ever make a mistake in this matter. Domestic animals sometimes make mistakes as to their food because their instinct has been tampered with and is by no means as sure as that of the wild creatures. It is said that sheep will occasionally eat laurel and St. John's-wort, which are poisonous to them. In the far West I was told that the horses sometimes eat a weed called the loco-weed that makes them crazy. I have since learned that the buffaloes and cattle with a strain of the buffalo blood never eat this weed.

The imitation among the lower animals to which I have referred is in no sense akin to teaching. The boy does not learn arithmetic by imitation. To teach is to bring one mind to act upon another mind; it is the result of a conscious effort on the part of both teacher and pupil. The child, says Darwin, has an instinctive tendency to speak, but not to brew, or bake, or write. The child comes to speak by imitation, as does the parrot, and then learns the meaning of words, as the parrot does not.

I am convinced there is nothing in the notion that animals consciously teach their young. Is it probable that a mere animal reflects upon the future any more than it does upon the past? Is it solicitous about the future well-being of its offspring any more than it is curious about its ancestry? Persons who think they see the lower animals training their young consciously or unconsciously supply something to their observations; they read their own thoughts or preconceptions into what they see. Yet so trained a naturalist and experienced a hunter as President Roosevelt differs with me in this matter. In a letter which I am permitted to quote, he says: —

"I have not the slightest doubt that there is a large amount of *unconscious* teaching by wood-folk of their offspring. In unfrequented places I have had the deer watch me with almost as much indifference as they do now in the Yellowstone Park. In frequented places, where they are hunted, young deer and young mountain sheep, on the other hand, — and of course young wolves, bobcats, and the like, — are exceedingly wary and shy when the sight or smell of man is concerned. Undoubtedly this is due to the fact that from their earliest moments of going about they learn to imitate the unflagging watchfulness of their parents, and by the exercise of some associative or imitative quality they grow to imitate and then to

A Fawn without Fear of Man

share the alarm displayed by the older ones at the smell or presence of man. A young deer that has never seen a man feels no instinctive alarm at his presence, or at least very little; but it will undoubtedly learn to associate extreme alarm with his presence from merely accompanying its mother, if the latter feels such alarm. I should not regard this as schooling by the parent any more than I should so regard the instant flight of twenty antelope who had not seen a hunter, because the twenty-first has seen him and has instantly run. Sometimes a deer or an antelope will deliberately give an alarm-cry at sight of something strange. This cry at once puts every deer or antelope on the alert; but they will be just as much on the alert if they witness nothing but an exhibition of fright and flight on the part of the first deer or antelope, without there being any conscious effort on its part to express alarm.

"Moreover, I am inclined to think that on certain occasions, rare though they may be, there is a conscious effort at teaching. I have myself known of one setter dog which would thrash its puppy soundly if the latter carelessly or stupidly flushed a bird. Something similar may occur in the wild state among such intelligent beasts as wolves and foxes. Indeed, I have some reason to believe that with both of these animals it does occur — that is, that there is conscious as well as unconscious teaching of the young in such matters as traps."

Probably the President and I differ more in the meaning we attach to the same words than in anything else. In a subsequent letter he says: "I think the chief difference between you and me in the matter is one of terminology. When I speak of unconscious teaching, I really mean simply acting in a manner which arouses imitation."

Imitation is no doubt the key to the whole matter. The animals unconsciously teach their young by their example, and in no other way. But I must leave the discussion of this subject for another chapter.

VI

ANIMAL COMMUNICATION

THE notion that animals consciously train and educate their young has been held only tentatively by European writers on natural history. Darwin does not seem to have been of this opinion at all. Wallace shared it at one time in regard to the birds, — their songs and nest-building, — but abandoned it later, and fell back upon instinct or inherited habit. Some of the German writers, such as Brehm, Büchner, and the Müllers, seem to have held to the notion more decidedly. But Professor Groos had not yet opened their eyes to the significance of the play of animals. The writers mentioned undoubtedly read the instinctive play of animals as an attempt on the part of the parents to teach their young.

That the examples of the parents in many ways stimulate the imitative instincts of the young is quite certain, but that the parents in any sense aim at instruction is an idea no longer held by writers on animal psychology.

Of course it all depends upon what we mean by teaching. Do we mean the communication of knowledge, or the communication of emotion? It seems to me that by teaching we mean the former. Man alone communicates knowledge; the lower animals communicate feeling or emotion. Hence their communications always refer to the present, never to the past or to the future.

That birds and beasts do communicate with each other, who can doubt? But that they impart knowledge, that they have any knowledge to impart, in the strict meaning of the word, any store of ideas or mental concepts — that is quite another matter. Teaching implies such store of ideas and power to impart them. The subconscious self rules in the animal; the conscious self rules in man, and the conscious self alone can teach or communicate knowledge. It seems to me that the cases of the deer and the antelope, referred to by President Roosevelt in the letter to me quoted in the last chapter, show the communication of emotion only.

Teaching implies reflection and judgment; it implies a thought of, and solicitude for, the future. "The young will need this knowledge," says the human parent, "and so we will impart it to them now." But the animal parent has consciously no knowledge to impart, only fear or suspicion. One may affirm almost anything of trained dogs and of dogs generally. I can well believe that the setter bitch spoken of by the President punished her pup when it flushed a bird, — she had been punished herself for the same offense, — but that the act was expressive of anything more than her present anger, that she was in any sense trying to train and instruct her pup, there is no proof.

But with animals that have not been to school to man, all ideas of teaching must be rudimentary indeed. How could a fox or a wolf instruct its young in such matters as traps? Only in the presence of the trap, certainly; and then the fear of the trap would be communicated to the young through natural instinct. Fear, like joy or curiosity, is contagious among beasts and birds, as it is among men; the young fox or wolf would instantly share the emotion of its parent in the presence of a trap. It is very important to the wild creatures that they have a quick apprehension of danger, and as a matter of fact they have. One wild and suspicious duck in a flock will often defeat the best laid plans of the duck-hunter. Its suspicions are quickly communicated to all its fellows: not through any conscious effort on its part to do so, but through the law of natural contagion above referred to. Where any bird or beast is much hunted, fear seems to be in the air, and their fellows come to be conscious of the danger which they have not experienced.

What an animal lacks in wit it makes up in caution. Fear is a good thing for the wild creatures to have in superabundance. It often saves them from real danger. But how undiscriminating it is! It is said that an iron hoop or wagon-tire placed around a setting hen in the woods will protect her from the foxes.

Animals are afraid on general principles. Anything new and strange excites their suspicions. In a herd of animals, cattle, or horses, fear quickly becomes a panic and rages like a conflagration. Cattlemen in the West found that any little thing at night might kindle the spark in their herds and sweep the whole mass away in a furious stampede. Each animal excites every other, and the multiplied fear of the herd is something terrible. Panics among men are not much different.

In a discussion like the present one, let us use words in their strict logical sense, if possible. Most of the current misconceptions in natural history, as in other matters, arise from a loose and careless use of words. One says teach and train and instruct, when the facts point to instinctive imitation or unconscious communication.

That the young of all kinds thrive better and develop more rapidly under the care of their parents than when deprived of that care is obvious enough. It would be strange if it were not so. Nothing can quite fill the place of the mother with either man or bird or beast. The mother provides and protects. The young quickly learn of her through the natural instinct of imitation. They share her fears, they follow in her footsteps, they look to her for protection;

it is the order of nature. They are not trained in the way they should go, as a child is by its human parents — they are not trained at all; but their natural instincts doubtless act more promptly and surely with the mother than without her. That a young kingfisher or a young osprey would, in due time, dive for fish, or a young marsh hawk catch mice and birds, or a young fox or wolf or coon hunt for its proper prey without the parental example, admits of no doubt at all; but they would each probably do this thing earlier and better in the order of nature than if that order were interfered with.

The other day I saw a yellow-bellied woodpecker alight upon a decaying beech and proceed to drill for a grub. Two of its fully grown young followed it and, alighting near, sidled up to where the parent was drilling. A hasty observer would say that the parent was giving its young a lesson in grub-hunting, but I read the incident differently. The parent bird had no thought of its young. It made passes at them when they came too near, and drove them away. Presently it left the tree, whereupon one of the young examined the hole its parent had made and drilled a little on its own account. A parental example like this may stimulate the young to hunt for grubs earlier than they would otherwise do, but this is merely conjecture. There is no proof of it, nor can there be any.

The mother bird or beast does not have to be

instructed in her maternal duties: they are instinctive with her; it is of vital importance to the continuance of the species that they should be. If it were a matter of instruction or acquired knowledge, how precarious it would be!

The idea of teaching is an advanced idea, and can come only to a being that is capable of returning upon itself in thought, and that can form abstract conceptions — conceptions that float free, so to speak, dissociated from particular concrete objects.

If a fox, or a wolf, for instance, were capable of reflection and of dwelling upon the future and upon the past, it might feel the need of instructing its young in the matter of traps and hounds, if such a thing were possible without language. When the cat brings her kitten a live mouse, she is not thinking about instructing it in the art of dealing with mice, but is intent solely upon feeding her young. The kitten already knows, through inheritance, about mice. So when the hen leads her brood forth and scratches for them, she has but one purpose — to provide them with food. If she is confined to the coop, the chickens go forth and soon scratch for themselves and snap up the proper insect food.

The mother's care and protection count for much, but they do not take the place of inherited instinct. It has been found that newly hatched chickens, when left to themselves, do not know the difference between edible and non-edible insects, but that they soon learn. In such matters the mother hen, no doubt, guides them.

A writer in "Forest and Stream," who has since published a book about his "wild friends," pushes this notion that animals train their young so far that it becomes grotesque. Here are some of the things that this keen observer and exposer of "false natural history" reports that he has seen about his cabin in the woods: He has seen an old crow that hurriedly flew away from his cabin door on his sudden appearance, return and beat its young because they did not follow quickly enough. He has seen a male chewink, while its mate was rearing a second brood, take the first brood and lead them away to a bird-resort (he probably meant to say to a bird-nursery or kinder-garten); and when one of the birds wandered back to take one more view of the scenes of its infancy, he has seen the father bird pounce upon it and give it a "severe whipping and take it to the resort again."

He has seen swallows teach their young to fly by gathering them upon fences and telegraph wires and then, at intervals (and at the word of command, I suppose), launching out in the air with them, and swooping and circling about. He has seen a song sparrow, that came to his dooryard for fourteen years (he omitted to say that he had branded him and so knew his bird), teach *his year-old boy to sing* (the italics are mine). This hermit-inclined sparrow wanted to "desert the fields for a life in the woods," but his "wife would not consent." Many a feather-less biped has had the same experience with his society-spoiled wife. The puzzle is, how did this masterly observer know that this state of affairs existed between this couple? Did the wife tell him, or the husband? "Hermit" often takes his visitors to a wood thrushes' singing-school, where, "as the birds forget their lesson, they drop out one by one."

He has seen an old rooster teaching a young rooster to crow! At first the old rooster crows mostly in the morning, but later in the season he crows throughout the day, at short intervals, to show the young "the proper thing." "Young birds re-moved out of hearing will not learn to crow." He hears the old grouse teaching the young to drum in the fall, though he neglects to tell us that he has seen the young in attendance upon these lessons. He has seen a mother song sparrow helping her two-year-old daughter build her nest. He has discov-ered that the cat talks to her kittens with her ears: when she points them forward, that means "yes;" when she points them backward, that means "no." Hence she can tell them whether the wagon they hear approaching is the butcher's cart or not, and thus save them the trouble of looking out.

And so on through a long list of wild and domes-tic creatures. At first I suspected this writer was covertly ridiculing a certain other extravagant "ob-server," but a careful reading of his letter shows him

to be seriously engaged in the worthy task of expos-
ing "false natural history."

Now the singing of birds, the crowing of cocks,
the drumming of grouse, are secondary sexual characteristics. They are not necessary to the lives of the
creatures, and are probably more influenced by imitation than are the more important instincts of self-
preservation and reproduction. Yet the testimony is
overwhelming that birds will sing and roosters crow
and turkeys gobble, though they have never heard
these sounds; and, no doubt, the grouse and the
woodpeckers drum from promptings of the same
sexual instinct.

I do not wish to accuse "Hermit" of willfully per-
verting the facts of natural history. He is one of
those persons who read their own fancies into whatever they look upon. He is incapable of disinterested
observation, which means he is incapable of observation at all in the true sense. There are no animals
that signal to each other with their ears. The movements of the ears follow the movements of the eye.
When an animal's attention is directed to any object or sound, its ears point forward; when its attention is relaxed, the ears fall. But with the cat tribe
the ears are habitually erect, as those of the horse
are usually relaxed. They depress them and revert
them, as do many other animals, when angered or
afraid.

Certain things in animal life lead me to suspect

that animals have some means of communication with one another, especially the gregarious animals, that is quite independent of what we mean by language. It is like an interchange or blending of subconscious states, and may be analogous to telepathy among human beings. Observe what a unit a flock of birds becomes when performing their evolutions in the air. They are not many, but one, turning and flashing in the sun with a unity and a precision that it would be hard to imitate. One may see a flock of shore-birds that behave as one body: now they turn to the sun a sheet of silver; then, as their dark backs are presented to the beholder, they almost disappear against the shore or the clouds. It would seem as if they shared in a communal mind or spirit, and that what one felt they all felt at the same instant.

In Florida I many times saw large schools of mullets fretting and breaking the surface of the water with what seemed to be the tips of their tails. A large area would be agitated and rippled by the backs or tails of a host of fishes. Then suddenly, while I looked, there would be one splash and every fish would dive. It was a multitude, again, acting as one body. Hundreds, thousands of tails slapped the water at the same instant and were gone.

When the passenger pigeons were numbered by millions, the enormous clans used to migrate from one part of the continent to another. I saw the last flight of them up the Hudson River valley in the spring of 1875. All day they streamed across the sky. One purpose seemed to animate every flock and every bird. It was as if all had orders to move to the same point. The pigeons came only when there was beech-mast in the woods. How did they know we had had a beech-nut year? It is true that a few straggling bands were usually seen some days in advance of the blue myriads: were these the scouts, and did they return with the news of the beech-nuts? If so, how did they communicate the intelligence and set the whole mighty army in motion?

The migrations among the four-footed animals that sometimes occur over a large part of the country — among the rats, the gray squirrels, the reindeer of the north — seem to be of a similar character. How does every individual come to share in the common purpose? An army of men attempting to move without leaders and without a written or spoken language becomes a disorganized mob. Not so the animals. There seems to be a community of mind among them in a sense that there is not among men. The pressure of great danger seems to develop in a degree this community of mind and feeling among men. Under strong excitement we revert more or less to the animal state, and are ruled by instinct. It may well be that telepathy — the power to project one's mental or emotional state so as to impress a friend at a distance — is a power which we have carried over from our remote animal ancestors. However this may be, it is certain that the sensitiveness of birds and quadrupeds to the condition of one another, their sense of a common danger, of food supplies, of the direction of home under all circumstances, point to the possession of a power which is only rudimentary in us.

Some observers explain these things on the theory that the flocks of birds have leaders, and that their surprising evolutions are guided by calls or signals from these leaders, too quick or too fine for our eyes or ears to catch. I suppose they would explain the movements of the schools of fish and the simultaneous movements of a large number of land animals on the same theory. I cannot accept this explanation. It is harder for me to believe that a flock of birds has a code of calls or signals for all its evolutions — now right, now left, now mount, now swoop — which each individual understands on the instant, or that the hosts of the wild pigeons had their captains and signals, than to believe that out of the flocking instinct there has grown some other instinct or faculty, less understood, but equally potent, that puts all the members of a flock in such complete rapport with one another that the purpose and the desire of one become the purpose and the desire of all. There is nothing in this state of things analogous to a military organization. The relation among the members of the flock is rather that of creatures sharing spontaneously the same subconscious or psychic state, and acted upon by the same hidden influence, in a way and to a degree that never occur among men.

The faculty or power by which animals find the way home over or across long stretches of country is quite as mysterious and incomprehensible to us as the spirit of the flock to which I refer. A hive of bees evidently has a collective purpose and plan that does not emanate from any single individual or group of individuals, and which is understood by all without outward communication.

Is there anything which, without great violence to language, may be called a school of the woods? In the sense in which a playground is a school — a playground without rules or methods or a director — there is a school of the woods. It is an unkept, an unconscious school or gymnasium, and is entirely instinctive. In play the young of all animals, no doubt, get a certain amount of training and disciplining that helps fit them for their future careers; but this school is not presided over or directed by parents, though they sometimes take part in it. It is spontaneous and haphazard, without rule or system; but is, in every case, along the line of the future struggle for life of the particular bird or animal. A young marsh hawk which we reared used to play at striking leaves or bits of bark with its talons; kittens play with a ball, or a cob, or a stick, as if it were a mouse; dogs race and wrestle with one another as in the chase; ducks dive and sport in the water; doves circle and dive in the air as if escaping from a hawk; birds pursue and dodge one another in the same way; bears wrestle and box; chickens have mimic battles; colts run and leap; fawns probably do the same thing; squirrels play something like a game of tag in the trees; lambs butt one another and skip about the rocks; and so on.

In fact, nearly all play, including much of that of man, takes the form of mock battle, and is to that extent an education for the future. Among the carnivora it takes also the form of the chase. Its spring and motive are, of course, pleasure, and not education; and herein again is revealed the cunning of nature — the power that conceals purposes of its own in our most thoughtless acts. The cat and the kitten play with the live mouse, not to indulge the sense of cruelty, as some have supposed, but to indulge in the pleasure of the chase and unconsciously to practice the feat of capture. The cat rarely plays with a live bird, because the recapture would be more difficult, and might fail. What fisherman would not like to take his big fish over and over again, if he could be sure of doing it, not from cruelty, but for the pleasure of practicing his art? For further light on the subject of the significance of the play of animals, I refer the reader to the work of Professor Karl Groos called "The Play of Animals."

ANIMAL COMMUNICATION

One of my critics has accused me of measuring all things by the standard of my little farm — of thinking that what is not true of animal life there is not true anywhere. Unfortunately my farm *is* small — hardly a score of acres — and its animal life very limited. I have never seen even a porcupine upon it; but I have a hill where one might roll down, should one ever come my way and be in the mood for that kind of play.[1] I have a few possums, a woodchuck or two, an occasional skunk, some red squirrels and rabbits, and many kinds of song-birds. Foxes occasionally cross my acres; and once, at least, I saw a bald eagle devouring a fish in one of my apple-trees. Wild ducks, geese, and swans in spring and fall pass across the sky above me. Quail and grouse invade my premises, and of crows I have, at least in bird-nesting time, too many.

But I have a few times climbed over my pasture wall and wandered into distant fields. Once upon a time I was a traveler in Asia for the space of two hours — an experience that ought to have yielded me some startling discoveries, but did not. Indeed, the wider I have traveled and observed nature, the more I am convinced that the wild creatures behave just about the same in all parts of the country; that is, under similar conditions. What one observes truly about bird or beast upon his farm of ten acres, he will not have to unlearn, travel as wide or as far as

[1] See comment on the story here alluded to on page 244.

101

he will. Where the animals are much hunted, they are of course much wilder and more cunning than where they are not hunted. In the Yellowstone National Park we found the elk, deer, and mountain sheep singularly tame; and in the summer, so we were told, the bears board at the big hotels. The wild geese and ducks, too, were tame; and the red-tailed hawk built its nest in a large dead oak that stood quite alone near the side of the road. With us the same hawk hides its nest in a tree in the dense woods, because the farmers unwisely hunt and destroy it. But the cougars and coyotes and bobcats were no tamer in the park than they are in other places where they are hunted.

Indeed, if I had elk and deer and caribou and moose and bears and wildcats and beavers and otters and porcupines on my farm, I should expect them to behave just as they do in other parts of the country under like conditions: they would be tame and docile if I did not molest them, and wild and fierce if I did. They would do nothing out of character in either case.

Your natural history knowledge of the East will avail you in the West. There is no country, says Emerson, in which they do not wash the pans and spank the babies; and there is no country where a dog is not a dog, or a fox a fox, or where a hare is ferocious, or a wolf lamblike. The porcupine behaves in the Rockies just as he does in the Catskills;

the deer and the moose and the black bear and the
beaver of the Pacific slope are almost identical in
their habits and traits with those of the Atlantic
slope.

In my observations of the birds of the far West,
I went wrong in my reckoning but once: the Western meadowlark has a new song. How or where he
got it is a mystery; it seems to be in some way the
gift of those great, smooth, flowery, treeless, dimpled
hills. But the swallow was familiar, and the robin
and the wren and the highhole, while the woodchuck I saw and heard in Wyoming might have
been the "chuck" of my native hills. The eagle is
an eagle the world over. When I was a boy I saw,
one autumn day, an eagle descend with extended
talons upon the backs of a herd of young cattle that
were accompanied by a cosset-sheep and were feeding upon a high hill. The object of the eagle seemed
to be to separate the one sheep from the cattle, or to
frighten them all into breaking their necks in trying
to escape him. But neither result did he achieve.
In the Yellowstone Park, President Roosevelt and
Major Pitcher saw a golden eagle trying the same
tactics upon a herd of elk that contained one yearling.
The eagle doubtless had his eye upon the yearling,
though he would probably have been quite satisfied to have driven one of the older ones down a
precipice. His chances of a dinner would have been
equally good.

There is one particular in which the bird families are much more human than our four-footed kindred. I refer to the practice of courtship. The male of all birds, so far as I know, pays suit to the female and seeks to please and attract her.[1] This the quadrupeds do not do; there is no period of courtship among them, and no mating or pairing as among the birds. The male fights for the female, but he does not seek to win her by delicate attentions. If there are any exceptions to this rule, I do not know them. There seems to be among the birds something that is like what is called romantic love. The choice of mate seems always to rest with the female,[1] while among the mammals the female shows no preference at all.

Among our own birds, the prettiest thing I know of attending the period of courtship, or preliminary to the match-making, is the spring musical festival and reunion of the goldfinches, which often lasts for days, through rain and shine. In April or May, apparently all the goldfinches from a large area collect in the top of an elm or a maple and unite in a prolonged musical festival. Is it a contest among the males for the favor of the females, or is it the spontaneous expression of the gladness of the whole clan at the return of the season of life and love? The birds seem to pair soon after, and doubtless the concert of voices has some reference to that event.

[1] Except in the case of certain birds of India and Australia.

ANIMAL COMMUNICATION

There is one other human practice often attributed to the lower animals that I must briefly consider, and that is the practice, under certain circumstances, of poisoning their young. One often hears of caged young birds being fed by their parents for a few days and then poisoned; or of a mother fox poisoning her captive young when she finds that she cannot liberate him; and such stories obtain ready credence with the public, especially with the young. To make these stories credible, one must suppose a school of pharmacy, too, in the woods.

"The worst thing about these poisoning stories," writes a friend of mine, himself a writer of nature-books, "is the implied appreciation of the full effect and object of poison — the comprehension by the fox, for instance, that the poisoned meat she may be supposed to find was placed there for the object of killing herself (or some other fox), and that she may apply it to another animal for that purpose. Furthermore, that she understands the nature of death — that it brings 'surcease of sorrow,' and that death is better than captivity for her young one. How did she acquire all this knowledge? Where was her experience of its supposed truth obtained? How could she make so fine and far-seeing a judgment, wholly out of the range of brute affairs, and so purely philosophical and humanly ethical? It violates every instinct and canon of natural law, which is for the preservation of life at all hazards.

This is simply the human idea of 'murder.' Animals kill one another for food, or in rivalry, or in blind ferocity of predatory disposition; but there is not a particle of evidence that they 'commit murder' for ulterior ends. It is questionable whether they comprehend the condition called death, or its nature, in any proper sense."

On another occasion I laughed at a recent nature writer for his credulity in half-believing the story told him by a fisherman, that the fox catches crabs by using his tail as a bait; and yet I read in Romanes that Olaus, in his account of Norway, says he has seen a fox do this very thing among the rocks on the sea-coast.[1] One would like to cross-question Olaus before accepting such a statement. One would as soon expect a fox to put his brush in the fire as in the water. When it becomes wet and bedraggled, he is greatly handicapped as to speed. There is no doubt that rats will put their tails into jars that contain liquid food they want, and then lick them off, as Romanes proved; but the rat's tail is not a brush, nor in any sense an ornament. Think what the fox-and-crab story implies! Now the fox is entirely a land animal, and lives by preying upon land crea-

[1] A book published in London in 1783, entitled *A Geographical, Historical, and Commercial Grammar and the Present State of the Several Kingdoms of the World*, among other astonishing natural history notes, makes this statement about the white and red fox of Norway: " They have a particular way of drawing crabs ashore by dipping their tails in the water, which the crab lays hold of."

tures, which it follows by scent or sight. It can neither see nor smell crabs in the deep water, where crabs are usually found. How should it know that there are such things as crabs? How should it know that they can be taken with bait and line or by fishing for them? When and how did it get this experience? This knowledge belongs to man alone. It comes through a process of reasoning that he alone is capable of. Man alone of land animals sets traps and fishes. There is a fish called the angler (*Lophius piscatorius*), which, it is said on doubtful authority, by means of some sort of appendages on its head angles for small fish; but no competent observer has reported any land animal doing so. Again, would a crab lay hold of a mass of fur like a fox's tail? — even if the tail could be thrust deep enough into the water, which is impossible. Crabs, when not caught with hand-nets, are usually taken in water eight or ten feet deep. They are baited and caught with a piece of meat tied to a string, but cannot be lifted to the surface till they are eating the meat, and then a dip-net is required to secure them. The story, on the whole, is one of the most preposterous that ever gained credence in natural history.

Good observers are probably about as rare as good poets. Accurate seeing, — an eye that takes in the whole truth, and nothing but the truth, — how rare indeed it is! So few persons know or can tell exactly what they see; so few persons can draw a right inference from an observed fact; so few persons can keep from reading their own thoughts and preconceptions into what they see ; only a person with the scientific habit of mind can be trusted to report things as they are. Most of us, in observing the wild life about us, see more or see less than the truth. We see less when our minds are dull, or preoccupied, or blunted by want of interest. This is true of most country people. We see more when we read the lives of the wild creatures about us in the light of our human experience, and impute to the birds and beasts human motives and methods. This is too often true of the eager city man or woman who sallies out into the country to study nature.

The tendency to sentimentalize nature has, in our time, largely taken the place of the old tendency to demonize and spiritize it. It is anthropomorphism in another form, less fraught with evil to us, but equally in the way of a clear understanding of the life about us.

VII

DEVIOUS PATHS

THERE is no better type or epitome of wild nature than the bird's-nest — something built, and yet as if it grew, a part of the ground, or of the rock, or of the branch upon which it is placed; beginning so coarsely, so irregularly, and ending so finely and symmetrically; so unlike the work of hands, and yet the result of a skill beyond hands; and when it holds its complement of eggs, how pleasing, how suggestive!

The bird adapts means to an end, and yet so differently from the way of man, — an end of which it does not know the value or the purpose. We know it is prompted to it by the instinct of reproduction. When the woodpecker in the fall excavates a lodge in a dry limb, we know he is prompted to it by the instinct of self-preservation, but the birds themselves obey the behests of nature without knowledge.

A bird's-nest suggests design, and yet it seems almost haphazard; the result of a kind of madness, yet with method in it. The hole the woodpecker drills for its cell is to the eye a perfect circle, and the rim of most nests is as true as that of a cup. The circle and the sphere exist in nature; they are mother forms and hold all other forms. They are easily attained; they are spontaneous and inevitable. The bird models her nest about her own breast; she turns round and round in it, and its circular character results as a matter of course. Angles, right lines, measured precision, so characteristic of the works of man, are rarely met with in organic nature.

Nature reaches her ends by devious paths; she loiters, she meanders, she plays by the way; she surely " arrives," but it is always in a blind, hesitating, experimental kind of fashion. Follow the tunnels of the ants or the crickets, or of the moles and the weasels, underground, or the courses of the streams or the paths of the animals above ground — how they turn and hesitate, how wayward and undecided they are! A right line seems out of the question.

The oriole often weaves strings into her nest; sometimes she binds and overhands the part of the rim where she alights in going in, to make it stronger, but it is always done in a hit-or-miss, childish sort of way, as one would expect it to be; the strings are massed, or snarled, or left dangling at loose ends, or are caught around branches; the weaving and the sewing are effective, and the whole nest is a marvel of blind skill, of untaught intelligence; yet how unmethodical, how delightfully irregular, how unmistakably a piece of wild nature!

Sometimes the instinct of the bird is tardy, and the egg of the bird gets ripe before the nest is ready; in such a case the egg is of course lost. I once found the nest of the black and white creeping warbler in a mossy bank in the woods, and under the nest was an egg of the bird. The warbler had excavated the site for her nest, dropped her egg into it, and then gone on with her building. Instinct is not always inerrant. Nature is wasteful, and plays the game with a free hand. Yet what she loses on one side she gains on another; she is like that least bittern Mr. Frank M. Chapman tells about. Two of the bittern's five eggs had been punctured by the long-billed marsh wren. When the bird returned to her nest and found the two eggs punctured, she made no outcry, showed no emotion, but deliberately proceeded to eat them. Having done this, she dropped the empty shells over the side of the nest, together with any straws that had become soiled in the process, cleaned her bill, and proceeded with her incubation. This was Nature in a nut-shell, — or rather egg-shell, — turning her mishaps to some good account. If the egg will not make a bird, it will make food; if not food, then fertilizer.

Among nearly all our birds, the female is the active business member of the partnership; she has a turn for practical affairs; she chooses the site of the nest, and usually builds it unaided. The life of the male is more or less a holiday or picnic till the young are hatched, when his real cares begin, for he does his part in feeding them. One may see the male cedar-bird attending the female as she is busy with her nest-building, but never, so far as I have observed, assisting her. One spring I observed with much interest a phœbe-bird building her nest not far from my cabin in the woods. The male looked on approvingly, but did not help. He perched most of the time on a mullein stalk near the little spring run where Phœbe came for mud. In the early morning hours she made her trips at intervals of a minute or two. The male flirted his tail and called encouragingly, and when she started up the hill with her load he would accompany her part way, to help her over the steepest part, as it were, then return to his perch and watch and call for her return. For an hour or more I witnessed this little play in bird life, in which the female's part was so primary and the male's so secondary. There is something in such things that seems to lend support to Professor Lester F. Ward's contention, as set forth in his "Pure Sociology," that in the natural evolution of the two sexes the female was first and the male second ; that he was made from her rib, so to speak, and not she from his.

With our phalarope and a few Australian birds, the position of the two sexes as indicated above is reversed, the females having the ornaments and bright colors and doing the courting, while the male does the incubating. In a few cases also the female is much the more masculine, noisy, and pugnacious. With some of our common birds, such as the woodpeckers, the chickadee, and the swallows, both sexes take part in nest-building.

It is a very pretty sight to witness a pair of wood thrushes building their nest. Indeed, what is there about the wood thrush that is not pleasing? He is a kind of visible embodied melody. Some birds are so sharp and nervous and emphatic in their movements, as the common snowbird or junco, the flashing of whose white tail quills expresses the character of the bird. But all the ways of the wood thrush are smooth and gentle, and suggest the melody of its song. It is the only bird thief I love to see carrying off my cherries. It usually takes only those dropped upon the ground by other birds, and with the red or golden globe impaled upon its beak, its flight across the lawn is a picture delightful to behold. One season a pair of them built a nest in a near-by grove; morning after morning, for many mornings, I used to see the two going to and from the nest, over my vineyard and currant patch and pear orchard, in quest of, or bringing material for, the structure. They flew low, the female in the lead, the male just behind in line with her, timing his motions to hers, the two making a brown, gently undulating line, very pretty to look upon, from my neighbor's field where they obtained the material, to the tree that held the nest. A gentle, gliding flight, hurried but hushed, as it were, and expressive of privacy and loving preoccupation. The male carried no material; apparently he was simply the escort of his mate; but he had an air of keen and joyous interest. He never failed to attend her each way, keeping about a yard behind her, and flying as if her thought were his thought and her wish his wish. I have rarely seen anything so pretty in bird life. The movements of all our thrushes except the robin give one this same sense of harmony, — nothing sharp or angular or abrupt. Their gestures are as pleasing as their notes.

One evening, while seated upon my porch, I had convincing proof that musical or song contests do take place among the birds. Two wood thrushes who had nests near by sat on the top of a dead tree and pitted themselves against each other in song for over half an hour, contending like champions in a game, and certainly affording the rarest treat in wood thrush melody I had ever had. They sang and sang with unwearied spirit and persistence, now and then changing position or facing in another direction, but keeping within a few feet of each other. The rivalry became so obvious and was so interesting that I finally made it a point not to take my eyes from the singers. The twilight deepened till their forms began to grow dim; then one of the

A Wood Thrush

Louis Agassiz Fuertes

birds could stand the strain no longer, the limit of fair competition had been reached, and seeming to say, " I will silence you, anyhow," it made a spiteful dive at its rival, and in hot pursuit the two disappeared in the bushes beneath the tree. Of course I would not say that the birds were consciously striving to outdo each other in song; it was the old feud between males in the love season, not a war of words or of blows, but of song. Had the birds been birds of brilliant plumage, the rivalry would probably have taken the form of strutting and showing off their bright colors and ornaments.

An English writer on birds, Edmund Selous, describes a similar song contest between two nightingales. " Jealousy," he says, " did not seem to blind them to the merit of each other's performance. Though often one, upon hearing the sweet, hostile strains, would burst forth instantly itself, — and here there was no certain mark of appreciation, — yet sometimes, perhaps quite as often, it would put its head on one side and listen with exactly the appearance of a musical connoisseur, weighing, testing, and appraising each note as it issued from the rival bill. A curious, half-suppressed expression would steal, or seem to steal (for Fancy may play her part in such matters), over the listening bird, and the idea appear to be, ' How exquisite would be those strains were they not sung by ——, and yet I must admit that they are exquisite.' " Fancy no doubt does play a part in such matters. It may well be doubted if birds are musical connoisseurs, or have anything like human appreciation of their own or of each other's songs. My reason for thinking so is this: I have heard a bobolink with an instrument so defective that its song was broken and inarticulate in parts, and yet it sang with as much apparent joy and abandon as any of its fellows. I have also heard a hermit thrush with a similar defect or impediment that appeared to sing entirely to its own satisfaction. It would be very interesting to know if these poor singers found mates as readily as their more gifted brothers. If they did, the Darwinian theory of "sexual selection" in such matters, according to which the finer songster would carry off the female, would fall to the ground. Yet it is certain that it is during the mating and breeding season that these "song combats" occur, and the favor of the female would seem to be the matter in dispute. Whether or not it be expressive of actual jealousy or rivalry, we have no other words to apply to it.

A good deal of light is thrown upon the ways of nature as seen in the lives of our solitary wasps, so skillfully and charmingly depicted by George W. Peckham and his wife in their work on those insects. So whimsical, so fickle, so forgetful, so fussy, so wise, and yet so foolish, as these little people are! such victims of routine and yet so individual, such apparent foresight and yet such thoughtlessness, at such great pains and labor to dig a hole and build a cell, and then at times sealing it up without storing it with food or laying the egg, half finishing hole after hole, and then abandoning them without any apparent reason; sometimes killing their spiders, at other times only paralyzing them; one species digging its burrow before it captures its game, others capturing the game and then digging the hole; some of them hanging the spider up in the fork of a weed to keep it away from the ants while they work at their nest, and running to it every few minutes to see that it is safe; others laying the insect on the ground while they dig; one species walking backward and dragging its spider after it, and when the spider is so small that it carries it in its mandible, still walking backward as if dragging it, when it would be much more convenient to walk forward. A curious little people, leading their solitary lives and greatly differentiated by the solitude, hardly any two alike, one nervous and excitable, another calm and unhurried; one careless in her work, another neat and thorough; this one suspicious, that one confiding; Ammophila using a pebble to pack down the earth in her burrow, while another species uses the end of her abdomen, — verily a queer little people, with a lot of wild nature about them, and a lot of human nature, too.

I think one can see how this development of individuality among the solitary wasps comes about. May it not be because the wasps are solitary ? They live alone. They have no one to imitate; they are uninfluenced by their fellows. No community interests override or check individual whims or peculiarities. The innate tendency to variation, active in all forms of life, has with them full sway. Among the social bees or wasps one would not expect to find those differences between individuals. The members of a colony all appear alike in habits and in dispositions. Colonies differ, as every bee-keeper knows, but probably the members composing it differ very little. The community interests shape all alike. Is it not the same in a degree among men ? Does not solitude bring out a man's peculiarities and differentiate him from others ? The more one lives alone, the more he becomes unlike his fellows. Hence the original and racy flavor of woodsmen, pioneers, lone dwellers in Nature's solitudes. Thus isolated communities develop characteristics of their own. Constant intercommunication, the friction of travel, of streets, of books, of newspapers, make us all alike ; we are, as it were, all pebbles upon the same shore, washed by the same waves.

Among the larger of vertebrate animals, I think, one might reasonably expect to find more individuality among those that are solitary than among those that are gregarious; more among birds of prey than among water-fowl, more among foxes than among prairie-dogs, more among moose than among sheep or buffalo, more among grouse than among quail. But I do not know that this is true.

Yet among none of these would one expect to find the diversity of individual types that one finds among men. No two dogs of the same breed will be found to differ as two men of the same family often differ. An original fox, or wolf, or bear, or beaver, or crow, or crab, — that is, one not merely different from his fellows, but obviously superior to them, differing from them as a master mind differs from the ordinary mind, — I think, one need not expect to find. It is quite legitimate for the animal-story writer to make the most of the individual differences in habits and disposition among the animals; he has the same latitude any other story writer has, but he is bound also by the same law of probability, the same need of fidelity to nature. If he proceed upon the theory that the wild creatures have as pronounced individuality as men have, that there are master minds among them, inventors and discoverers of new ways, born captains and heroes, he will surely " o'erstep the modesty of nature."

The great diversity of character and capacity among men doubtless arises from their greater and more complex needs, relations, and aspirations. The animals' needs in comparison are few, their relations simple, and their aspirations *nil*. One cannot see what could give rise to the individual types and exceptional endowments that are often claimed for them. The law of variation, as I have said, would give rise to differences, but not to a sudden reversal of race habits, or to animal geniuses.

The law of variation is everywhere operative — less so now, no doubt, than in the earlier history of organic life on the globe. Yet Nature is still experimenting in her blind way, and hits upon many curious differences and departures. But I suppose if the race of man were exterminated, man would never arise again. I doubt if the law of evolution could ever again produce him, or any other species of animal.

This principle of variation was no doubt much more active back in geologic time, during the early history of animal life upon the globe, than it is in this late age. And for the reason that animal life was less adapted to its environment than it is now, the struggle for life was sharper. Perfect adaptation of any form of life to the conditions surrounding it seems to check variability. Animal and plant life seem to vary more in this country than in England because the conditions of life are harder. The extremes of heat and cold, of wet and dry, are much greater. It has been found that the eggs of the English sparrow vary in form and color more in the United States than in Great Britain. Certain American shells are said to be more variable than the English. Among our own birds it has been found that the "migratory species evince a greater amount of individual variation than do non-migrating species" because they are subject to more varying conditions of food and climate. I think we may say, then, if there were no struggle for life, if uniformity of temperature and means of subsistence everywhere prevailed, there would be little or no variation and no new species would arise. The causes of variation seem to be the inequality and imperfection of things; the pressure of life is unequally distributed, and this is one of Nature's ways that accounts for much that we see about us.

VIII

WHAT DO ANIMALS KNOW?

AFTER the discussion carried on in the foregoing chapters touching the general subject of
animal life and instinct, we are prepared, I think, to
ask with more confidence, What do animals know?

The animals unite such ignorance with such
apparent knowledge, such stupidity with such clev-
erness, that in our estimate of them we are likely
to rate their wit either too high or too low. With
them, knowledge does not fade into ignorance, as
it does in man; the contrast is like that between
night and day, with no twilight between. So keen
one moment, so blind the next!

Think of the ignorance of the horse after all his
long association with man; of the trifling things
along the street at which he will take fright, till he
rushes off in a wild panic of fear, endangering his
own neck and the neck of his driver. One would
think that if he had a particle of sense he would
know that an old hat or a bit of paper was harmless.
But fear is deeply implanted in his nature; it has
saved the lives of his ancestors countless times, and
it is still one of his ruling passions.

I have known a cow to put her head between two trees in the woods — a kind of natural stanchion — and not have wit enough to get it out again, though she could have done so at once by lifting her head to a horizontal position. But the best instance I know of the grotesque ignorance of a cow is given by Hamerton in his "Chapters on Animals." The cow would not "give down" her milk unless she had her calf before her. But her calf had died, so the herdsman took the skin of the calf, stuffed it with hay, and stood it up before the inconsolable mother. Instantly she proceeded to lick it and to yield her milk. One day, in licking it, she ripped open the seams, and out rolled the hay. This the mother at once proceeded to eat, without any look of surprise or alarm. She liked hay herself, her acquaintance with it was of long standing, and what more natural to her than that her calf should turn out to be made of hay! Yet this very cow that did not know her calf from a bale of hay would have defended her young against the attack of a bear or a wolf in the most skillful and heroic manner; and the horse that was nearly frightened out of its skin by a white stone, or by the flutter of a piece of newspaper by the roadside, would find its way back home over a long stretch of country, or find its way to water in the desert, with a certainty you or I could not approach.

The hen-hawk that the farm-boy finds so difficult to approach with his gun will yet alight upon his steel trap fastened to the top of a pole in the fields. The rabbit that can be so easily caught in a snare or in a box-trap will yet conceal its nest and young in the most ingenious manner. Where instinct or inherited knowledge can come into play, the animals are very wise, but new conditions, new problems, bring out their ignorance.

A college girl told me an incident of a red squirrel she had observed at her home in Iowa that illustrates how shallow the wit of a squirrel is when confronted by new conditions. This squirrel carried nuts all day and stored them in the end of a drain-pipe that discharged the rain-water upon the pavement below. The nuts obeyed the same law that the rain-water did, and all rolled through the pipe and fell upon the sidewalk. In the squirrel's experience, and in that of his forbears, all holes upon the ground were stopped at the far end, or they were like pockets, and if nuts were put in them they stayed there. A hollow tube open at both ends, that would not hold nuts — this was too much for the wit of the squirrel. But how wise he is about the nuts themselves!

Among the lower animals the ignorance of one is the ignorance of all, and the knowledge of one is the knowledge of all, in a sense in which the same is not true among men. Of course some are more stupid than others of the same species, but probably, on the one hand, there are no idiots among them, and, on the other, none is preëminent in wit.

Animals take the first step in knowledge — they perceive things and discriminate between them; but they do not take the second step — combine them, analyze them, and form concepts and judgments.

So that, whether animals know much or little, I think we are safe in saying that what they know in the human way, that is, from a process of reasoning, is very slight.

The animals all have in varying degrees perceptive intelligence. They know what they see, hear, smell, feel, so far as it concerns them to know it. They know their kind, their mates, their enemies, their food, heat from cold, hard from soft, and a thousand other things that it is important that they should know, and they know these things just as we know them, through their perceptive powers.

We may ascribe intelligence to the animals in the same sense in which we ascribe it to a child, as the perception of the differences or of the likenesses and the relations of things — that is, perceptive intelligence, but not reasoning intelligence. When the child begins to "notice things," to know its mother, to fear strangers, to be attracted by certain objects, we say it begins to show intelligence. Development in this direction goes on for a long time before it can form any proper judgment about things or take the step of reason.

If we were to subtract from the sum of the intelligence of an animal that which it owes to nature or inherited knowledge, the amount left, representing its own power of thought, would be very small. Darwin tells of a pike in an aquarium separated by plate-glass from fish which were its proper food, and that the pike, in trying to capture the fish, would often dash with such violence against the glass as to be completely stunned. This the pike did for three months before it learned caution. After the glass was removed, the pike would not attack those particular fishes, but would devour others that were introduced. It did not yet understand the situation, but merely associated the punishment it had received with a particular kind of fish.

During the mating season the males of some of our birds may often be seen dashing themselves against a window, and pecking and fluttering against the pane for hours at a time, day after day. They take their own images reflected in the glass to be rival birds, and are bent upon demolishing them. They never comprehend the mystery of the glass, because glass is not found in nature, and neither they nor their ancestors have had any experience with it.

Contrast these incidents with those which Darwin relates of the American monkeys. When the monkeys had cut themselves once with any sharp tool, they would not touch it again, or else would handle it with the greatest caution. They evinced the simpler forms of reason, of which monkeys are no doubt capable.

Animals are wise as Nature is wise; they partake, each in its own measure, of that universal intelligence, or mind-stuff, that is operative in all things — in the vegetable as well as in the animal world. Does the body, or the life that fills it, reason when it tries to get rid of, or to neutralize the effects of, a foreign substance, like a bullet, by encysting it? or when it thickens the skin on the hand or on any other part of the body, even forming special pads called callosities, as a result of the increased wear or friction? This may be called physiological intelligence.

But how blind this intelligence is at times, or how wanting in judgment, may be seen when it tries to develop a callosity upon the foot as a result of the friction of the shoe, and overdoes the matter and produces the corn. The corn is a physiological blunder. Or see an unexpected manifestation of this intelligence when we cut off the central and leading shoot of a spruce or of a pine tree, and straightway one of the lateral and horizontal branches rises up, takes the place of the lost leader, and carries the tree upward; or in the roots of a tree working their way through the ground much like molten metal, parting and uniting, taking the form of whatever object they touch, shaping themselves to the rock, flowing into its seams, the better to get a grip upon the earth and thus maintain an upright position.

In the animal world this foresight becomes psychic

intelligence, developing in man the highest form of all, reasoned intelligence. When an animal solves a new problem or meets a new condition as effectually as the tree or the body does in the cases I have just cited, we are wont to ascribe to it powers of reason. Reason we may call it, but it is reason not its own.

This universal or cosmic intelligence makes up by far the greater part of what animals know. The domestic animals, such as the dog, that have long been under the tutelage of man, of course show more independent power of thought than the uneducated beasts of the fields and woods.

The plant is wise in all ways to reproduce and perpetuate itself; see the many ingenious devices for scattering seed. In the animal world this intelligence is most keen and active in the same direction. The wit of the animal comes out most clearly in looking out for its food and safety. We are often ready to ascribe reason to it in feats shown in these directions.

In man alone does this universal intelligence or mind-stuff reach out beyond these primary needs and become aware of itself. What the plant or the animal does without thought or rule, man takes thought about. He considers his ways. I noticed that the scallops in the shallow water on the beach had the power to anchor themselves to stones or to some other object, by putting out a little tough but elastic cable from near the hinge, and that they did so when

the water was rough; but I could not look upon it
as an act of conscious or individual intelligence on
the part of the bivalve. It was as much an act of the
general intelligence to which I refer as was its hinge
or its form. But when the sailor anchors his ship,
that is another matter. He thinks about it, he reasons from cause to effect, he sees the storm coming,
he has a fund of experience, and his act is a special
individual act.

The muskrat builds its house instinctively, and
all muskrats build alike. Man builds his house
from reason and forethought. Savages build as
nearly alike as the animals, but civilized man shows
an endless variety. The higher the intelligence, the
greater the diversity.

The sitting bird that is so solicitous to keep its
eggs warm, or to feed and defend its young, probably shows no more independent and individual
intelligence than the plant that strives so hard to ma-
ture and scatter its seed. A plant will grow toward
the light; a tree will try to get from under another
tree that overshadows it; a willow will run its roots
toward the water: but these acts are the results of
external stimuli alone.

When I go to pass the winter in a warmer climate,
the act is the result of calculation and of weighing
pros and cons. I can go, or I can refrain from going. Not so with the migrating birds. Nature plans
and thinks for them; it is not an individual act on

the part of each; it is a race instinct: they must go; the life of the race demands it. Or when the old goose covers up her nest, or the rabbit covers her young with a blanket of hair and grass of her own weaving, I do not look upon these things as independent acts of intelligence: it is the cunning of nature; it is a race instinct.

Animals, on the whole, know what is necessary for them to know — what the conditions of life have taught their ancestors through countless generations. It is very important, for instance, that amphibians shall have some sense that shall guide them to the water; and they have such a sense. It is said that young turtles and crocodiles put down anywhere will turn instantly toward the nearest water. It is certain that the beasts of the field have such a sense much more fully developed than has man. It is of vital importance that birds should know how to fly, how to build their nests, how to find their proper food, and when and where to migrate, without instruction or example, otherwise the race might become extinct.

Richard Jefferies says that most birds'-nests need a structure around them like a cage to keep the young from falling out or from leaving the nest prematurely. Now, if such a structure were needed, either the race of birds would have failed, or the structure would have been added. Since neither has happened, we are safe in concluding it is not needed.

We are not warranted in attributing to any wild, untrained animal a degree of intelligence that its forbears could not have possessed. The animals for the most part act upon inherited knowledge, that is, knowledge that does not depend upon instruction or experience. For instance, the red squirrels near me seem to know that chestnut-burs will open if cut from the tree and allowed to lie upon the ground. At least, they act upon this theory. I do not suppose this fact or knowledge lies in the squirrel's mind as it would in that of a man — as a deduction from facts of experience or of observation. The squirrel cuts off the chestnuts because he is hungry for them, and because his ancestors for long generations have cut them off in the same way. That the air or sun will cause the burs to open is a bit of knowledge that I do not suppose he possesses in the sense in which we possess it: he is in a hurry for the nuts, and does not by any means always wait for the burs to open; he frequently chips them up and eats the pale nuts.

The same squirrel will bite into the limbs of a maple tree in spring and suck the sap. What does he know about maple trees and the spring flow of sap? Nothing as a mental concept, as a bit of concrete knowledge. He often finds the sap flowing from a crack or other wound in the limbs of a maple, and he sips it and likes it. Then he sinks his teeth into the limb, as his forbears undoubtedly did.

WHAT DO ANIMALS KNOW?

When I was a boy and saw, as I often did on my way to school, where a squirrel had stopped on his course through the woods and dug down through two or three feet of snow, bringing up a beech-nut or an acorn, I used to wonder how he knew the nut was there. I am now convinced that he smelled it.

Why should he not? It stands the squirrel in hand to smell nuts; they are his life. He knows a false nut from a good one without biting into it. Try the experiment upon your tame chipmunk or caged gray squirrel, and see if this is not so. The false or dead nut is lighter, and most persons think this fact guides the squirrel. But this, it seems to me, implies an association of ideas beyond the reach of instinct. A young squirrel will reject a worthless nut as promptly as an old one will. Again the sense of smell is the guide; the sound-meated nut has an odor which the other has not. All animals are keen and wise in relation to their food and to their natural enemies. A red squirrel will chip up green apples and pears for the seeds at the core: can he know, on general principles, that these fruits contain seeds? Does not some clue to them reach his senses?

I have known gray squirrels to go many hundred yards in winter across fields to a barn that contained grain in the sheaf. They could have had no other guide to the grain than the sense of smell. Watch a chipmunk or any squirrel near at hand: as a friend of mine observed, he seems to be smelling with his whole body; his abdomen fairly palpitates with the effort.

The coon knows when the corn is in the milk, gaining that knowledge, no doubt, through his nose. At times he seems to know enough, too, to cut off his foot when caught in a trap, especially if the foot becomes frozen; but if you tell me he will treat his wound by smearing it with pitch or anything else, or in any way except by licking it, I shall discredit you. The practice of the art of healing by the application of external or foreign substances is a conception entirely beyond the capacity of any of the lower animals. If such a practice had been necessary for the continuance of the species, it would probably have been used. The knowledge it implies could not be inherited; it must needs come by experience. When a fowl eats gravel or sand, is it probable that the fowl knows what the practice is for, or has any notion at all about the matter? It has a craving for the gravel, that is all. Nature is wise for it.

The ostrich is described by those who know it intimately as the most stupid and witless of birds, and yet before leaving its eggs exposed to the hot African sun, the parent bird knows enough to put a large pinch of sand on the top of each of them, in order, it is said, to shade and protect the germ, which always rises to the highest point of the egg. This act certainly cannot be the result of knowledge, as we use the term; the young ostrich does it as well as the old. It is the inherited wisdom of the race, or instinct.

A sitting bird or fowl turns its eggs at regular intervals, which has the effect of keeping the yolk from sticking to the shell. Is this act the result of knowledge or of experience? It is again the result of that untaught knowledge called instinct. Some kinds of eggs hatch in two weeks, some in three, others in four. The mother bird has no knowledge of this period. It is not important that she should have. If the eggs are addled or sterile, she will often continue to sit beyond the normal period. If the continuance of the species depended upon her knowing the exact time required to hatch her eggs, as it depends upon her having the incubating fever, of course she would know exactly, and would never sit beyond the required period.

But what shall we say of Mrs. Annie Martin's story, in her "Home Life on an Ostrich Farm," of the white-necked African crow that, in order to feast upon the eggs of the ostrich, carries a stone high in the air above them and breaks them by letting it fall? This looks like reason, a knowledge of the relation of cause and effect. Mrs. Martin says the crows break tortoise-shells in the same way, and have I not heard of our own crows and gulls carrying clams and crabs into the air and dropping them upon the rocks?

If Mrs. Martin's statements are literally true, — if she has not the failing, so common among women observers, of letting her feeling and her fancies color her observations, — then her story shows how the pressure of hunger will develop the wit of a crow.

But the story goes one step beyond my credence. It virtually makes the crow a tool-using animal, and Darwin knew of but two animals, the man-like ape and the elephant, that used anything like a tool or weapon to attain their ends. How could the crow gain the knowledge or the experience which this trick implies? What could induce it to make the first experiment of breaking an egg with a falling stone but an acquaintance with physical laws such as man alone possesses? The first step in this chain of causation it is easy to conceive of any animal taking ; namely, the direct application of its own powers or weapons to the breaking of the shell. But the second step, — the making use of a foreign substance or object in the way described, — that is what staggers one.

Our own crow has great cunning, but it is only cunning. He is suspicious of everything that looks like design, that suggests a trap, even a harmless string stretched around a corn-field. As a natural philosopher he makes a poor show, and the egg or the shell that he cannot open with his own beak he leaves behind. Yet even his alleged method of dropping clams upon the rocks to break the shells does not seem incredible. He might easily drop a clam by accident, and then, finding the shell broken, repeat the experiment. He is still only taking the first step in the sequence of causations.

A recent English nature-writer, on the whole, I think, a good observer and truthful reporter, Mr. Richard Kearton, tells of an osprey that did this incredible thing: to prevent its eggs from being harmed by an enforced exposure to the sun, the bird plunged into the lake, then rose, and shook its dripping plumage over the nest. The writer apparently reports this story at second-hand. It is incredible to me, because it implies a knowledge that the hawk could not possibly possess.

Such an emergency could hardly arise once in a lifetime to it or its forbears. Hence the act could not have been the result of inherited habit, or instinct, and as an original act on the part of the osprey it is not credible. The bird probably plunged into the lake for a fish, and then by accident shook itself above the eggs. In any case, the amount of water that would fall upon the eggs under such circumstances would be too slight to temper appreciably the heat.

There is little doubt that among certain of our common birds the male, during periods of excessive heat, has been known to shade the female with his outstretched wings, and the mother bird to shade her young in the same way. But this is a different matter. This emergency must have occurred for ages, and it, again, called only for the first step from cause to effect, and called for the use of no intermediate agent. If the robin were to hold a leaf or a branch above his mate at such times, that would imply reflection.

It is said that elephants in India will besmear themselves with mud as a protection against insects, and that they will break branches from the trees and use them to brush away the flies. If this is true, it shows, I think, something beyond instinct in the elephant; it shows reflection.

All birds are secretive about their nests, and display great cunning in hiding them; but whether they know the value of adaptive material, such as moss, lichens, and dried grass, in helping to conceal them, admits of doubt, because they so often use the results of our own arts, as paper, rags, strings, tinsel, in such a reckless way. In a perfectly wild state they use natural material because it is the handiest and there is really no other. The phœbe uses the moss on or near the rocks where she builds; the sparrows, the bobolinks, and the meadowlarks use the dry grass of the bank or of the meadow bottom where the nest is placed.

The English writer to whom I have referred says that the wren builds the outside of its nest of old hay straws when placing it in the side of a rick, of green moss when it is situated in a mossy bank, and of dead leaves when in a hedge-row or a bramble-bush, in each case thus rendering the nest very difficult of detection because it harmonizes so perfectly with its surroundings, and the writer wonders if this harmony is the result of accident or of design. He is inclined to think that it is unpremeditated, as I myself do. The bird uses the material nearest to hand.

Another case, which this same writer gives at second-hand, of a bird recognizing the value of protective coloration, is not credible. A friend of his told him that he had once visited a colony of terns "on an island where the natural breeding accommodation was so limited that many of them had conveyed patches of pebbles on to the grass and laid their eggs thereon."

Here is the same difficulty we have encountered before — one more step of reasoning than the bird is capable of. As a deduction from observed facts, a bird, of course, knows nothing about protective coloring; its wisdom in this respect is the wisdom of Nature, and Nature in animal life never acts with this kind of foresight. A bird may exercise some choice about the background of its nest, but it will not make both nest and background.

Nature learns by endless experiment. Through a long and expensive process of natural selection she seems to have brought the color of certain animals and the color of their environment pretty close together, the better to hide the animals from their enemies and from their prey, as we are told; but the animals themselves do not know this, though they may act as if they did. Young terns and gulls instinctively squat upon the beach, where their colors so harmonize with the sand and pebbles that the birds are virtually invisible. Young partridges do the same in the woods, where the eye cannot tell the reddish tuft of down from the dry leaves. How many gulls and terns and partridges were sacrificed before Nature learned this trick!

I regard the lower animals as incapable of taking the step from the fact to the principle. They have perceptions, but not conceptions. They may recognize a certain fact, but any deduction from that fact to be applied to a different case, or to meet new conditions, is beyond them. Wolves and foxes soon learn to be afraid of poisoned meat: just what gives them the hint it would be hard to say, as the survivors could not know the poison's deadly effect from experience; their fear of it probably comes from seeing their fellows suffer and die after eating it, or maybe through that mysterious means of communication between animals to which I have referred in a previous article. The poison probably changes the odor of the meat, and this strange smell would naturally put them on their guard.

We do not expect rats to succeed in putting a bell on the cat, but if they were capable of conceiving such a thing, that would establish their claim to be regarded as reasonable beings. I should as soon expect a fox or a wolf to make use of a trap to capture its prey as to make use of poison in any way. Why does not the fox take a stick and spring the trap he is so afraid of? Simply because the act would involve a mental process beyond him. He has not yet learned to use even the simplest implement to attain his end. Then he would probably be just as afraid of the trap after it was sprung as before. He in some way associates it with his arch-enemy, man.

Such stories, too, as a chained fox or a coyote getting possession of corn or other grain and baiting the chickens with it — feigning sleep till the chicken gets within reach, and then seizing it — are of the same class, incredible because transcending the inherited knowledge of those animals. I can believe that a fox might walk in a shallow creek to elude the hound, because he may inherit this kind of cunning, and in his own experience he may have come to associate loss of scent with water. Animals stalk their prey, or lie in wait for it, instinctively, not from a process of calculation, as man does. If a fox would bait poultry with corn, why should he not, in his wild state, bait mice and squirrels with nuts and seeds? Has a cat ever been known to bait a rat with a piece of cheese?

Animals seem to have a certain association of ideas; one thing suggests another to them, as with us. This fact is made use of by animal-trainers. I can easily believe the story Charles St. John tells of the fox he saw waylaying some hares, and which, to screen himself the more completely from his quarry, scraped a small hollow in the ground and threw up the sand about it. But if St. John had said that the fox brought weeds or brush to make himself a blind, as the hunter often does, I should have discredited him, just as I discredit the observation of a man quoted by Romanes, who says that jackals, ambushing deer at the latter's watering-place, deliberately wait till the deer have filled themselves with water, knowing that in that state they are more easily run down and captured!

President Roosevelt, in "The Wilderness Hunter," — a book, by the way, of even deeper interest to the naturalist than to the sportsman, — says that the moose has to the hunter the "very provoking habit of making a half or three-quarters circle before lying down, and then crouching with its head so turned that it can surely perceive any pursuer who may follow its trail." This is the cunning of the moose developed through long generations of its hunted and wolf-pursued ancestors, — a cunning that does not differ from that of a man under the same circumstances, though, of course, it is not the result of the same process of reasoning.

I have known a chipping sparrow to build her nest on a grape-vine just beneath a bunch of small green grapes. Soon the bunch grew and lengthened and filled the nest, crowding out the bird. If the bird could have foreseen the danger, she would have shown something like human reason.

Birds that nest along streams, such as the water-thrush and the water-ouzel, I suppose are rarely ever brought to grief by high water. They have learned through many generations to keep at a safe distance. I have never known a woodpecker to drill its nesting-cavity in a branch or limb that was ready to fall. Not that woodpeckers look the branch or tree over with a view to its stability, but that they will cut into a tree only of a certain hardness; it is a family instinct. Birds sometimes make the mistake of building their nests on slender branches that a summer tempest will turn over, thus causing the eggs or the young to spill upon the ground. Even instinct cannot always get ahead of the weather.

It is almost impossible for us not to interpret the lives of the lower animals in the terms of our own experience and our own psychology. I entirely agree with Lloyd Morgan that we err when we do so, when we attribute to them what we call sentiments or any of the emotions that spring from our moral and æsthetic natures, — the sentiments of justice, truth, beauty, altruism, goodness, duty, and the like, — because these sentiments are the products of concepts and ideas to which the brute natures are strangers. But all the emotions of our animal nature — fear, anger, curiosity, local attachment, jealousy, and rivalry — are undoubtedly the same in the lower orders.

Though almost anything may be affirmed of dogs, for they are nearly half human, yet I doubt if even dogs experience the feeling of shame or guilt or revenge that we so often ascribe to them. These feelings are all complex and have a deep root. When I was a youth, my father had a big churn-dog that appeared one morning with a small bullet-hole in his hip. Day after day the old dog treated his wound with his tongue, after the manner of dogs, until it healed, and the incident was nearly forgotten. One day a man was going by on horseback, when the old dog rushed out, sprang at the man, and came near pulling him from the horse. It turned out that this was the person who had shot the dog, and the dog recognized him.

This looks like revenge, and it would have been such in you or me, but in the dog it was probably simple anger at the sight of the man who had hurt him. The incident shows memory and the association of impressions, but the complex feeling of vengeance, as we know it, is another matter.

If animals do not share our higher intellectual nature, we have no warrant for attributing to them anything like our higher and more complex emotional nature. Musical strains seem to give them pain rather than pleasure, and it is quite evident that perfumes have no attraction for them.

WHAT DO ANIMALS KNOW?

The stories, which seem to be well authenticated, of sheep-killing dogs that have slipped their collars in the night and indulged their passion for live mutton, and then returned and thrust their necks into their collars before their absence was discovered, do not, to my mind, prove that the dogs were trying to deceive their masters and conceal their guilt, but rather show how obedient to the chain and collar the dogs had become. They had long been subject to such control and discipline, and they returned to them again from the mere force of habit.

I do not believe even the dog to be capable of a sense of guilt. Such a sense implies a sense of duty, and this is a complex ethical sense that the animals do not experience. What the dog fears, and what makes him put on his look of guilt and shame, is his master's anger. A harsh word or a severe look will make him assume the air of a culprit whether he is one or not, and, on the other hand, a kind word and a reassuring smile will transform him into a happy beast, no matter if the blood of his victim is fresh upon him.

A dog is to be broken of a bad habit, if at all, not by an appeal to his conscience or to his sense of duty, for he has neither, but by an appeal to his susceptibility to pain.

Both Pliny and Plutarch tell the story of an elephant which, having been beaten by its trainer for its poor dancing, was afterward found all by itself practicing its steps by the light of the moon. This is just as credible as many of the animal stories one hears nowadays.

Many of the actions of the lower animals are as automatic as those of the tin rooster that serves as a weather-vane. See how intelligently the rooster acts, always pointing the direction of the wind without a moment's hesitation. Or behold the vessel anchored in the harbor, how intelligently it adjusts itself to the winds and the tides! I have seen a log, caught in an eddy in a flooded stream, apparently make such struggles to escape that the thing became almost uncanny in its semblance to life. Man himself often obeys just such unseen currents of race or history when he thinks he is acting upon his own initiative.

When I was in Alaska, I saw precipices down which hundreds of horses had dashed themselves in their mad and desperate efforts to escape from the toil and suffering they underwent on the White Pass trail. Shall we say these horses deliberately committed suicide? Suicide it certainly was in effect, but of course not in intention. What does or can a horse know about death, or about self-destruction? These animals were maddened by their hardships, and blindly plunged down the rocks.

The tendency to humanize the animals is more and more marked in all recent nature books that aim at popularity. A recent British book on animal life has a chapter entitled "Animal Materia Medica." The writer, to make out his case, is forced to treat as medicine the salt which the herbivorous animals eat, and the sand and gravel which grain and nut-eating birds take into their gizzards to act as mill-stones to grind their grist. He might as well treat their food as medicine and be done with it. So far as I know, animals have no remedies whatever for their ailments. Even savages have, for the most part, only "fake" medicines.

A Frenchman has published a book, which has been translated into English, on the "Industries of Animals." Some of these Frenchmen could give points even to our "Modern School of Nature Study." It may be remembered that Michelet said the bird floated, and that it could puff itself up so that it was lighter than the air! Not a little contemporary natural science can beat the bird in this respect.

The serious student of nature can have no interest in belittling or in exaggerating the intelligence of animals. What he wants is the truth about them, and this he will not get from our natural history romancers, nor from the casual, untrained observers, who are sure to interpret the lives of the wood-folk in terms of their own motives and experiences, nor from Indians, trappers, or backwoodsmen, who give such free rein to their fancies and superstitions.

Such a book as Romanes's "Animal Intelligence"

is not always a safe guide. It is like a lawyer's plea to the jury for his client. Romanes was so intent upon making out his case that he allowed himself to be imposed upon by the tales of irresponsible observers. Many of his stories of the intelligence of birds and beasts are antecedently improbable. He evidently credits the story of the Bishop of Carlisle, who thinks he saw a jackdaw being tried by a jury of rooks for some misdemeanor. Jack made a speech and the jury cawed back at him, and after a time appeared to acquit Jack! What a child's fancy to be put in a serious work on "Animal Intelligence"! The dead birds we now and then find hanging from the nest, or from the limb of a tree, with a string wound around their necks are no doubt criminals upon whom their fellows have inflicted capital punishment!

Most of the observations upon which Romanes bases his conclusions are like the incident which he quoted from Jesse, who tells of some swallows that in the spirit of revenge tore down a nest from which they had been ejected by the sparrows, in order to destroy the young of their enemies — a feat impossible for swallows to do. Jesse does not say he saw the swallows do it, but he "saw the young sparrows dead upon the ground amid the ruins of the nest," and of course the nest could get down in no other way!

Not to Romanes or Jesse or Michelet must we go

for the truth about animals, but to the patient, honest Darwin, to such calm, keen, and philosophical investigators as Lloyd Morgan, and to the books of such sportsmen as Charles St. John, or to our own candid, trained, and many-sided Theodore Roosevelt, — men capable of disinterested observation, with no theories about animals to uphold.

IX

DO ANIMALS THINK AND REFLECT?

WHEN we see the animals going about, living their lives in many ways as we live ours, seeking their food, avoiding their enemies, building their nests, digging their holes, laying up stores, migrating, courting, playing, fighting, showing cunning, courage, fear, joy, anger, rivalry, grief, profiting by experience, following their leaders, — when we see all this, I say, what more natural than that we should ascribe to them powers akin to our own, and look upon them as thinking, reasoning, and reflecting. A hasty survey of animal life is sure to lead to this conclusion. An animal is not a clod, nor a block, nor a machine. It is alive and self-directing, it has some sort of psychic life, yet the more I study the subject, the more I am persuaded that with the probable exception of the dog on occasions, and of the apes, animals do not think or reflect in any proper sense of those words. As I have before said, animal life shows in an active and free state that kind of intelligence that pervades and governs the whole organic world, — intelligence that takes no thought of itself. Here, in front of my window, is a black raspberry bush. A few weeks ago its branches curved upward, with their ends swinging fully two feet above the ground; now those ends are thrust down through the weeds and are fast rooted to the soil. Did the raspberry bush think, or choose what it should do? Did it reflect and say, Now is the time for me to bend down and thrust my tip into the ground? To all intents and purposes yes, yet there was no voluntary mental process, as in similar acts of our own. We say its nature prompts it to act thus and thus, and that is all the explanation we can give. Or take the case of the pine or the spruce tree that loses its central and leading shoot. When this happens, does the tree start a new bud and then develop a new shoot to take the place of the lost leader? No, a branch from the first ring of branches below, probably the most vigorous of the whorl, is promoted to the leadership. Slowly it rises up, and in two or three years it reaches the upright position and is leading the tree upward. This, I suspect, is just as much an act of conscious intelligence and of reason as is much to which we are so inclined to apply those words in animal life. I suppose it is all foreordained in the economy of the tree, if we could penetrate that economy. It is in this sense that Nature thinks in the animal, and the vegetable, and the mineral worlds. Her thinking is more flexible and adaptive in the vegetable than in the mineral, and more so in the animal than in the vegetable, and the most so of all in the mind of man.

The way the wild apple trees and the red thorn trees in the pasture, as described by Thoreau, triumph over the cattle that year after year browse them down, suggests something almost like human tactics. The cropped and bruised tree, not being allowed to shoot upward, spreads more and more laterally, thus pushing its enemies farther and farther away, till, after many years, a shoot starts up from the top of the thorny, knotted cone, and in one season, protected by this *cheval-de-frise*, attains a height beyond the reach of the cattle, and the victory is won. Now the whole push of the large root system goes into the central shoot and the tree is rapidly developed.

This almost looks like a well-laid scheme on the part of the tree to defeat its enemies. But see how inevitable the whole process is. Check the direct flow of a current and it will flow out at the sides ; check the side issues and they will push out on their sides, and so on. So it is with the tree or seedling. The more it is cropped, the more it branches and rebranches, pushing out laterally as its vertical growth is checked, till it has surrounded the central stalk on all sides with a dense, thorny hedge. Then as this stalk is no longer cropped, it leads the tree upward. The lateral branches are starved, and in a few years the tree stands with little or no evidence of the ordeal it has passed through. In like manner the nature of the animals prompts them to the deeds they do, and we think of them as the result of a mental process, because similar acts in ourselves are the result of such a process.

See how the mice begin to press into our buildings as the fall comes on. Do they know winter is coming? In the same way the vegetable world knows it is coming when it prepares for winter, or the insect world when it makes ready, but not as you and I know it. The woodchuck "holes up" in late September; the crows flock and select their rookery about the same time, and the small wood newts or salamanders soon begin to migrate to the marshes. They all know winter is coming, just as much as the tree knows, when in August it forms its new buds for the next year, or as the flower knows that its color and perfume will attract the insects, and no more. The general intelligence of nature settles all these and similar things.

When a bird selects a site for its nest, it seems, on first view, as if it must actually think, reflect, compare, as you and I do when we decide where to place our house. I saw a little chipping sparrow trying to decide between two raspberry bushes. She kept going from one to the other, peering, inspecting, and apparently weighing the advantages of each. I saw a robin in the woodbine on the side of the house trying to decide which particular place was the best site

Woodchucks sitting in front of their Hole

for her nest. She hopped to this tangle of shoots and sat down, then to that, she turned around, she readjusted herself, she looked about, she worked her feet beneath her, she was slow in making up her mind. Did she make up her mind? Did she think, compare, weigh? I do not believe it. When she found the right conditions, she no doubt felt pleasure and satisfaction, and that settled the question. An inward, instinctive want was met and satisfied by an outward material condition. In the same way the hermit crab goes from shell to shell upon the beach, seeking one to its liking. Sometimes two crabs fall to fighting over a shell that each wants. Can we believe that the hermit crab thinks and reasons? It selects the suitable shell instinctively, and not by an individual act of judgment. Instinct is not always inerrant, though it makes fewer mistakes than reason does. The red squirrel usually knows how to come at the meat in the butternut with the least gnawing, but now and then he makes a mistake and strikes the edge of the kernel, instead of the flat side. The cliff swallow will stick her mud nest under the eaves of a barn where the boards are planed so smooth that the nest sooner or later is bound to fall. She seems to have no judgment in the matter. Her ancestors built upon the face of high cliffs, where the mud adhered more firmly.

A wood thrush began a nest in one of my maples, as usual making the foundation of dry leaves, bits of paper, and dry grass. After the third day the site on the branch was bare, the wind having swept away every vestige of the nest. As I passed beneath the tree I saw the thrush standing where the nest had been, apparently in deep thought. A few days afterward I looked again, and the nest was completed. The bird had got ahead of the wind at last. The nesting-instinct had triumphed over the weather.

Take the case of the little yellow warbler when the cowbird drops her egg into its nest — does anything like a process of thought or reflection pass in the bird's mind then? The warbler is much disturbed when she discovers the strange egg, and her mate appears to share her agitation. Then after a time, and after the two have apparently considered the matter together, the mother bird proceeds to bury the egg by building another nest on top of the old one. If another cowbird's egg is dropped in this one, she will proceed to get rid of this in the same way. This all looks very like reflection. But let us consider the matter a moment. This thing between the cowbird and the warbler has been going on for innumerable generations. The yellow warbler seems to be the favorite host of this parasite, and something like a special instinct may have grown up in the warbler with reference to this strange egg. The bird reacts, as the psychologists say, at sight of **it,** then she proceeds to dispose of it in the way above described. *All yellow warblers act in the same manner*, which is the way of instinct. Now if this procedure was the result of an individual thought or calculation on the part of the birds, they would not all do the same thing ; different lines of conduct would be hit upon. How much simpler and easier it would be to throw the egg out — how much more like an act of rational intelligence. So far as I know, no bird does eject this parasitical egg, and no other bird besides the yellow warbler gets rid of it in the way I have described. I have found a deserted phœbe's nest with one egg of the phœbe and one of the cowbird in it.

Some of our wild birds have changed their habits of nesting, coming from the woods and the rocks to the protection of our buildings. The phœbe-bird and the cliff swallow are marked examples. We ascribe the change to the birds' intelligence, but to my mind it shows only their natural adaptiveness. Take the cliff swallow, for instance; it has largely left the cliffs for the eaves of our buildings. How naturally and instinctively this change has come about! In an open farming country insect life is much more varied and abundant than in a wild, unsettled country. This greater food supply naturally attracts the swallows. Then the protecting eaves of the buildings would stimulate their nesting-instincts. The abundance of mud along the highways and about the farm would also no doubt have its effect, and the birds would adopt the new sites as a matter of course. Or take the phœbe, which originally built its nest under ledges, and does so still to some extent. It, too, would find a more abundant food supply in the vicinity of farm-buildings and bridges. The protected nesting-sites afforded by sheds and porches would likewise stimulate its nesting-instincts, and attract the bird as we see it attracted each spring.

Nearly everything an animal does is the result of an inborn instinct acted upon by an outward stimulus. The margin wherein intelligent choice plays a part is very small. But it does at times play a part — perceptive intelligence, but not rational intelligence. The insects do many things that look like intelligence, yet how these things differ from human intelligence may be seen in the case of one of our solitary wasps, — the mud-dauber, — which sometimes builds its cell with great labor, then seals it up without laying its egg and storing it with the accustomed spiders. Intelligence never makes that kind of a mistake, but instinct does. Instinct acts more in the invariable way of a machine. Certain of the solitary wasps bring their game — spider, or bug, or grasshopper — and place it just at the entrance of their hole, and then go into their den apparently to see that all is right before they carry it in.

Fabre, the French naturalist, experimented with one of these wasps, as follows: While the wasp was in its den he moved its grasshopper a few inches away. The wasp came out, brought it to the opening as before, and went within a second time; again the game was removed, again the wasp came out and brought it back and entered her nest as before. This little comedy was repeated over and over; each time the wasp felt compelled to enter her hole before dragging in the grasshopper. She was like a machine that would work that way and no other. Step must follow step in just such order. Any interruption of the regular method and she must begin over again. This is instinct, and the incident shows how widely it differs from conscious intelligence.

If you have a tame chipmunk, turn him loose in an empty room and give him some nuts. Finding no place to hide them, he will doubtless carry them into a corner and pretend to cover them up. You will see his paws move quickly about them for an instant as if in the act of pulling leaves or mould over them. His machine, too, must work in that way. After the nuts have been laid down, the next thing in order is to cover them, and he makes the motions all in due form. Intelligence would have omitted this useless act.

A canary-bird in its cage will go through all the motions of taking a bath in front of the cup that holds its drinking-water when it can only dip its bill into the liquid. The sight or touch of the water excites it and sets it going, and with now and then a drop thrown from its beak it will keep up the flirting and fluttering motion of its tail and wings precisely as if taking a real instead of an imaginary bath.

Attempt to thwart the nesting-instinct in a bird and see how persistent it is, and how blind! One spring a pair of English sparrows tried to build a nest on the plate that upholds the roof of my porch. They were apparently attracted by an opening about an inch wide in the top of the plate, that ran the whole length of it. The pair were busy nearly the whole month of April in carrying nesting-material to various points on that plate. That big crack or opening which was not large enough to admit their bodies seemed to have a powerful fascination for them. They carried straws and weed stalks and filled up one portion of it, and then another and another, till the crack was packed with rubbish from one end of the porch to the other, and the indignant broom of the housekeeper grew tired of sweeping up the litter. The birds could not effect an entrance into the interior of the plate, but they could thrust in their nesting-material, and so they persisted week after week, stimulated by the presence of a cavity beyond their reach. The case is a good illustration of the blind working of instinct.

Animals have keen perceptions, — keener in many respects than our own, — but they form no conceptions, have no powers of comparing one thing with another. They live entirely in and through their senses.

DO ANIMALS THINK AND REFLECT?

It is as if the psychic world were divided into two planes, one above the other, — the plane of sense and the plane of spirit. In the plane of sense live the lower animals, only now and then just breaking for a moment into the higher plane. In the world of sense man is immersed also — this is his start and foundation; but he rises into the plane of spirit, and here lives his proper life. He is emancipated from sense in a way that beasts are not.

Thus, I think, the line between animal and human psychology may be pretty clearly drawn. It is not a dead-level line. Instinct is undoubtedly often modified by intelligence, and intelligence is as often guided or prompted by instinct, but one need not hesitate long as to which side of the line any given act of man or beast belongs. When the fox resorts to various tricks to outwit and delay the hound (if he ever consciously does so), he exercises a kind of intelligence, — the lower form which we call cunning, — and he is prompted to this by an instinct of self-preservation. When the birds set up a hue and cry about a hawk or an owl, or boldly attack him, they show intelligence in its simpler form, the intelligence that recognizes its enemies, prompted again by the instinct of self-preservation. When a hawk does not know a man on horseback from a horse, it shows a want of intelligence. When a crow is kept away from a corn-field by a string stretched around it, the fact shows how masterful is its fear and how shallow its wit. When a cat or a dog, or a horse or a cow, learns to open a gate or a door, it shows a degree of intelligence — power to imitate, to profit by experience. A machine could not learn to do this. If the animal were to close the door or gate behind it, that would be another step in intelligence. But its direct wants have no relation to the closing of the door, only to the opening of it. To close the door involves an after-thought that an animal is not capable of. A horse will hesitate to go upon thin ice or upon a frail bridge, even though it has never had any experience with thin ice or frail bridges. This, no doubt, is an inherited instinct, which has arisen in its ancestors from their fund of general experience with the world. How much with them has depended upon a secure footing! A pair of house wrens had a nest in my well-curb; when the young were partly grown and heard any one come to the curb, they would set up a clamorous calling for food. When I scratched against the sides of the curb beneath them like some animal trying to climb up, their voices instantly hushed; the instinct of fear promptly overcame the instinct of hunger. Instinct is intelligent, but it is not the same as acquired individual intelligence; it is untaught.

When the nuthatch carries a fragment of a hickory-nut to a tree and wedges it into a crevice in the bark, the bird is not showing an individual act of intelligence : all nuthatches do this ; it is a race instinct. The act shows intelligence, — that is, it adapts means to an end, — but it is not like human or individual intelligence, which adapts new means to old ends, or old means to new ends, and which springs up on the occasion. Jays and chickadees hold the nut or seed they would peck under the foot, but the nuthatch makes a vise to hold it of the bark of the tree, and one act is just as intelligent as the other; both are the promptings of instinct. But when man makes a vise, or a wedge, or a bootjack, he uses his individual intelligence. When the jay carries away the corn you put out in winter and hides it in old worms' nests and knot-holes and crevices in trees, he is obeying the instinct of all his tribe to pilfer and hide things, — an instinct that plays its part in the economy of nature, as by its means many acorns and chestnuts get planted and large seeds widely disseminated. By this greed of the jay the wingless nuts take flight, oaks are planted amid the pines, and chestnuts amid the hemlocks.

Speaking of nuts reminds me of an incident I read of the deer or white-footed mouse — an incident that throws light on the limitation of animal intelligence. The writer gave the mouse hickory-nuts, which it attempted to carry through a crack between the laths in the kitchen wall. The nuts were too large to go through the crack. The mouse would try to push them through; failing in that, he would go through and then try to pull them after him. All night he or his companion seems to have kept up this futile attempt, fumbling and dropping the nut every few minutes. It never occurred to the mouse to gnaw the hole larger, as it would instantly have done had the hole been too small to admit its own body. It could not project its mind thus far; it could not get out of itself sufficiently to regard the nut in its relation to the hole, and it is doubtful if any four-footed animal is capable of that degree of reflection and comparison. Nothing in its own life or in the life of its ancestors had prepared it to meet that kind of a difficulty with nuts. And yet the writer who made the above observation says that when confined in a box, the sides of which are of unequal thickness, the deer mouse, on attempting to gnaw out, almost invariably attacks the thinnest side. How does he know which is the thinnest side? Probably by a delicate and trained sense of feeling or hearing. In gnawing through obstructions from within, or from without, he and his kind have had ample experience.

Now when we come to insects, we find that the above inferences do not hold. It has been observed that when a solitary wasp finds its hole in the ground too small to admit the spider or other insect which it has brought, it falls to and enlarges it. In this and in other respects certain insects seem to take the step of reason that quadrupeds are incapable of.

Lloyd Morgan relates at some length the experiments he tried with his fox terrier, Tony, seeking to teach him how to bring a stick through a fence with vertical palings. The spaces would allow the dog to pass through, but the palings caught the ends of the stick which the dog carried in his mouth. When his master encouraged him, he pushed and struggled vigorously. Not succeeding, he went back, lay down, and began gnawing the stick. Then he tried again, and stuck as before, but by a chance movement of his head to one side finally got the stick through. His master patted him approvingly and sent him for the stick again. Again he seized it by the middle, and of course brought up against the palings. After some struggles he dropped it and came through without it. Then, encouraged by his master, he put his head through, seized the stick, and tried to pull it through, dancing up and down in his endeavors. Time after time and day after day the experiment was repeated with practically the same results. The dog never mastered the problem. He could not see the relation of that stick to the opening in the fence. At one time he worked and tugged three minutes trying to pull the stick through. Of course, if he had had any mental conception of the problem or had thought about it at all, a single trial would have convinced him as well as would a dozen trials. Mr. Morgan tried the experiment with other dogs with like result. When they did get the stick through, it was always by chance.

It has never been necessary that the dog or his ancestors should know how to fetch long sticks through a narrow opening in a fence. Hence he does not know the trick of it. But we have a little bird that knows the trick. The house wren will carry a twig three inches long through a hole of half that diameter. She knows how to manage it because the wren tribe have handled twigs so long in building their nests that this knowledge has become a family instinct.

What we call the intelligence of animals is limited for the most part to sense perception and sense memory. We teach them certain things, train them to do tricks quite beyond the range of their natural intelligence, not because we enlighten their minds or develop their reason, but mainly by the force of habit. Through repetition the act becomes automatic. Who ever saw a trained animal, unless it be the elephant, do anything that betrayed the least spark of conscious intelligence? The trained pig, or the trained dog, or the trained lion does its "stunt" precisely as a machine would do it — without any more appreciation of what it is doing. The trainer and public performer find that things must always be done in the same fixed order; any change, anything unusual, any strange sound, light, color, or movement, and trouble at once ensues.

DO ANIMALS THINK AND REFLECT?

I read of a beaver that cut down a tree which was held in such a way that it did not fall, but simply dropped down the height of the stump. The beaver cut it off again; again it dropped and refused to fall; he cut it off a third and a fourth time: still the tree stood. Then he gave it up. Now, so far as I can see, the only independent intelligence the animal showed was when it ceased to cut off the tree. Had it been a complete automaton, it would have gone on cutting — would it not? — till it made stove-wood of the whole tree. It was confronted by a new problem, and after a while it took the hint. Of course it did not understand what was the matter, as you and I would have, but it evidently concluded that something was wrong. Was this of itself an act of intelligence? Though it may be that its ceasing to cut off the tree was simply the result of discouragement, and involved no mental conclusion at all. It is a new problem, a new condition, that tests an animal's intelligence. How long it takes a caged bird or beast to learn that it cannot escape! What a man would see at a glance it takes weeks or months to pound into the captive bird, or squirrel, or coon. When the prisoner ceases to struggle, it is probably not because it has at last come to understand the situation, but because it is discouraged. It is checked, but not enlightened.

Even so careful an observer as Gilbert White credits the swallow with an act of judgment to which it is not entitled. He says that in order that the mud nest may not advance too rapidly and so fall of its own weight, the bird works at it only in the morning, and plays and feeds the rest of the day, thus giving the mud a chance to harden. Had not the genial parson observed that this is the practice of all birds during nest-building—that they work in the early morning hours and feed and amuse themselves the rest of the day? In the case of the mud-builders, this interim of course gives the mud a chance to harden, but are we justified in crediting them with this forethought?

Such skill and intelligence as a bird seems to display in the building of its nest, and yet at times such stupidity! I have known a phœbe-bird to start four nests at once, and work more or less upon all of them. She had deserted the ancestral sites under the shelving rocks and come to a new porch, upon the plate of which she started her four nests. She blundered because her race had had little or no experience with porches. There were four or more places upon the plate just alike, and whichever one of these she chanced to strike with her loaded beak she regarded as the right one. Her instinct served her up to a certain point, but it did not enable her to discriminate between those rafters. Where a little original intelligence should have come into play she was deficient. Her progenitors had built under rocks where there was little chance for mistakes of this sort, and they had learned through ages of experience to blend the nest with its surroundings, by the use of moss, the better to conceal it. My phœbe brought her moss to the new timbers of the porch, where it had precisely the opposite effect to what it had under the gray mossy rocks.

I was amused at the case of a robin that recently came to my knowledge. The bird built its nest in the south end of a rude shed that covered a table at a railroad terminus upon which a locomotive was frequently turned. When her end of the shed was turned to the north she built another nest in the temporary south end, and as the reversal of the shed ends continued from day to day, she soon had two nests with two sets of eggs. When I last heard from her, she was consistently sitting on that particular nest which happened to be for the time being in the end of the shed facing toward the south. The bewildered bird evidently had had no experience with the tricks of turn-tables!

An intelligent man once told me that crabs could reason, and this was his proof: In hunting for crabs in shallow water, he found one that had just cast its shell, but the crab put up just as brave a fight as ever, though of course it was powerless to inflict any pain; as soon as the creature found that its bluff game did not work, it offered no further resistance. Now I should as soon say a wasp reasoned because a stingless drone, or male, when you capture him, will make all the motions with its body, curving and thrusting, that its sting-equipped fellows do. This action is from an inherited instinct, and is purely automatic. The wasp is not putting up a bluff game; it is really trying to sting you, but has not the weapon. The shell-less crab quickly reacts at your approach, as is its nature to do, and then quickly ceases its defense because in its enfeebled condition the impulse of defense is feeble also. Its surrender was on physiological, not upon rational grounds.

Thus do we without thinking impute the higher faculties to even the lowest forms of animal life. Much in our own lives is purely automatic — the quick reaction to appropriate stimuli, as when we ward off a blow, or dodge a missile, or make ourselves agreeable to the opposite sex; and much also is inherited or unconsciously imitative.

Because man, then, is half animal, shall we say that the animal is half man? This seems to be the logic of some people. The animal man, while retaining much of his animality, has evolved from it higher faculties and attributes, while our four-footed kindred have not thus progressed.

Man is undoubtedly of animal origin, but his rise occurred when the principle of variation was much more active, when the forms and forces of nature were much more youthful and plastic, when the seething and fermenting of the vital fluids were at a high pitch in the far past, and it was high tide with the creative impulse. The world is aging, and, no doubt, the power of initiative in Nature is becoming less and less. I think it safe to say that the worm no longer aspires to be man.

X

A PINCH OF SALT

PROBABLY I have become unusually cautious of late about accepting offhand all I read in print on subjects of natural history. I take much of it with a liberal pinch of salt. Newspaper reading tends to make one cautious — and who does not read newspapers in these days? One of my critics says, apropos of certain recent strictures of mine upon some current nature writers, that I discredit whatever I have not myself seen; that I belong to that class of observers "whose view-point is narrowed to the limit of their own personal experience." This were a grievous fault if it were true, so much we have to take upon trust in natural history as well as in other history, and in life in general. "Mr. Burroughs might have remembered," says another critic discussing the same subject, "that nobody has seen quite so many things as everybody." How true! If I have ever been guilty of denying the truth of what everybody has seen, my critic has just ground for complaint. I was conscious, in the paper referred to,[1] of denying only the truth of certain

---

[1] *Atlantic Monthly*, March, 1903.

things that one man alone had reported having seen, — things so at variance not only with my own observations, but with those of all other observers and with the fundamental principles of animal psychology, that my " will to believe," always easy to move, balked and refused to take a step.

In matters of belief in any field, it is certain that the scientific method, the method of proof, is not of equal favor with all minds. Some persons believe what they can or must, others what they would. One person accepts what agrees with his reason and experience, another what is agreeable to his or her fancy. The grounds of probability count much with me; the tone and quality of the witness count for much. Does he ring true? Is his eye single? Does he see out of the back of his head? — that is, does he see on more than one side of a thing? Is he in love with the truth, or with the strange, the bizarre? Last of all, my own experience comes in to correct or to modify the observations of others. If what you report is antecedently improbable, I shall want concrete proof before accepting it, and I shall cross-question your witness sharply. If you tell me you have seen apples and acorns, or pears and plums, growing upon the same tree, I shall discredit you. The thing has never been known and is contrary to nature. But if you tell me you have seen a peach tree bearing nectarines, or have known a nectarine-stone to produce a peach tree, I shall still want to cross-question you sharply, but I may believe you. Such things have happened. Or if you tell me that you have seen an old doe with horns, or a hen with spurs, or a male bird incubating and singing on the nest, unusual as the last occurrence is, I shall not dispute you. I will concede that you may have seen a white crow or a white blackbird or a white robin, or a black chipmunk or a black red squirrel, and many other departures from the usual in animal life; but I cannot share the conviction of the man who told me he had seen a red squirrel curing rye before storing it up in its den, or of the writer who believes the fox will ride upon the back of a sheep to escape the hound, or of another writer that he has seen the blue heron chumming for fish. Even if you aver that you have seen a woodpecker running down the trunk of a tree as well as up, I shall be sure you have not seen correctly. It is the nuthatch and not the woodpecker that hops up and down and around the trees. It is easy to transcend any man's experience; not so easy to transcend his reason. "Nobody has seen so many things as everybody," yet a dozen men cannot see any farther than one, and the truth is not often a matter of majorities. If you tell me any incident in the life of bird or beast that implies the possession of what we mean by reason, I shall be very skeptical.

Am I guilty, then, as has been charged, of preferring the deductive method of reasoning to the more modern and more scientific inductive method? But I doubt if the inductive method would avail one in trying to prove that the old cow really jumped over the moon. We do deny certain things upon general principles, and affirm others. I do not believe that a rooster ever laid an egg, or that a male tiger ever gave milk. If your alleged fact contradicts fundamental principles, I shall beware of it; if it contradicts universal experience, I shall probe it thoroughly. A college professor wrote me that he had seen a crow blackbird catch a small fish and fly away with it in its beak. Now I have never seen anything of the kind, but I know of no principle upon which I should feel disposed to question the truth of such an assertion. I have myself seen a crow blackbird kill an English sparrow. Both proceedings I think are very unusual, but neither is antecedently improbable. If the professor had said that he saw the blackbird dive head first into the water for the fish, after the manner of the kingfisher, I should have been very skeptical. He only saw the bird rise up from the edge of the water with the wriggling fish in its mouth. It had doubtless seized it in shallow water near the shore. But I should discredit upon general principles the statement of the woman who related with much detail how she and her whole family had seen a pair "of small brown birds" carry their half-fledged young from their nest in a low bush, where there was danger from cats, to a new nest which they had just finished in the top of a near-by tree! Could any person who knows the birds credit such a tale? The bank-teller throws out the counterfeit coin or bill because his practiced eye and touch detect the fraud at once. On similar grounds the experienced observer rejects all such stories as the above. Darwin quotes an authority for the statement that our ruffed grouse makes its drumming sound by striking its wings together over its back. A recent writer says the sound is not made with the wings at all, but is made with the voice, just as a rooster crows. Every woodsman knows that neither statement is true, and he knows it, not on general principles, but from experience — he has seen the grouse drum.

Birds that are not flycatchers sometimes take insects in the air; they do it clumsily, but they get the bug. On the other hand, flycatchers sometimes eat fruit. I have seen the kingbird carry off raspberries. All such facts are matters of observation. In the search for truth we employ both the deductive and the inductive methods; we deduce principles from facts, and we test alleged facts by principles.

The other day an intelligent woman told me this about a canary-bird: The bird had a nest with young in the corner of her cage; near by were some other birds in a cage — I forget what they were; they had a full view of all the domestic affairs of the canary. This publicity she evidently did not like, for she tore out of the paper that covered the bottom of her cage a piece as large as one's hand and wove it into the wires so as to make a screen against her inquisitive neighbors. My informant evidently believed this story. It was agreeable to her fancies and feelings. But see the difficulties in the way. How could the bird with its beak tear out a broad piece of paper? then, how could it weave it into the wires of its cage? Furthermore, the family of birds to which the canary belongs are not weavers; they build cup-shaped nests, and they have had no use for screens or covers, and they never have made them. Just what was the truth about the matter I cannot say, but if we know anything about animal psychology, we know that was not the truth. It is always risky to attribute to an animal any act its ancestors could not have performed.

Again, things are reported as facts that are not so much contrary to reason as contrary to all experience, and with these, too, I have my difficulties. A recent writer upon our wild life says he has discovered that the cowbird watches over its young and assists the foster-parents in providing food for them — an observation so contrary to all that we know of parasitical birds, both at home and abroad, that no real observer can credit the statement. Our cowbird has been under observation for a hundred years or more; every dweller in the country must see one or more young cowbirds being fed by their foster-parents every season, yet no competent observer has ever reported any care of the young bird by its real parent. If this were true, it would make the cowbird only half parasitical — an unheard-of phenomenon.

The same writer tells this incident about a grouse that had a nest near his cabin. One morning he heard a strange cry in the direction of the nest, and taking the path that led to it, he met the grouse running toward him with one wing pressed close to her side, and fighting off two robber crows with the other. Under the closed wing the grouse was carrying an egg, which she had managed to save from the ruin of her nest. The bird was coming to the hermit for succor. Now, am I skeptical about such a story, put down in apparent good faith in a book of natural history as a real occurrence, because I have never seen the like? No; I am skeptical because the incident is so contrary to all that we know about grouse and all other wild birds. Our belief in nearly all matters takes the line of least resistance, and it is easier for me to believe that the writer deceived himself, than that such a thing ever happened. In the first place, a grouse could not pick up an egg with her wing when crows were trying to rob her, and, in the second place, she would not think far enough to do it if she had the power. What was she going to do with the egg? Bring it to the hermit for his breakfast? This last supposition is just as reasonable as any part of the story. A grouse will not readily leave her unfledged young, but she will leave her eggs when disturbed by man or beast with apparent unconcern.

It is the rarest thing in the world that real observers see any of these startling and exceptional things in nature. Thoreau saw none. White saw none. Charles St. John saw none. John Muir reports none, Audubon none. It is always your untrained observer that has his poser, his shower of frogs or lizards, or his hoop snakes, and the like. The impossible things that country people see or hear of would make a book of wonders. In some places fishermen believe that the loon carries its egg under its wing till it hatches, and one would say that they are in a position to know. So they are. But opportunity is only half the problem; the verifying mind is the other half. One of our writers of popular nature books relates this curious incident of "animal surgery" among wild ducks. He discovered two eider ducks swimming about a fresh-water pond and acting queerly, "dipping their heads under water and keeping them there for a minute or more at a time." He later discovered that the ducks had large mussels attached to their tongues, and that they were trying to get rid of them by drowning them. The birds had discovered that the salt-water mussel cannot live in fresh water. Now am I to accept this story without question because I find it printed in a book? In the first place, is it not most remarkable that if the ducks had discovered that the bivalves could not live in fresh water, they should not also have discovered that they could not live in the air? In fact, that they would die as soon in the air as in the fresh water?[1] See how much trouble the ducks could have saved themselves by going and sitting quietly upon the beach, or putting their heads under their wings and going to sleep on the wave. Oysters are often laid down in fresh water to "fatten" before being sent to market, and probably mussels would thrive for a short time in fresh water equally well. In the second place, a duck's tongue is a very short and stiff affair, and is fixed in the lower mandible as in a trough. Ducks do not protrude the tongue when they feed; they cannot protrude it; and if a duck can crush a mussel-shell with its beak, what better position could it have the bivalve in than fast to the tongue between the upper and the lower mandible? The story is certainly a very "fishy" one. In all such cases the mind follows the line of least resistance. If the ducks were deliberately holding their bills under water, it is easier to believe that they did it because they thereby found some relief from pain, than that they knew the bivalves would let go their hold

[1] I have tried the experiment on two ordinary clams, and they both died on the third day.

sooner in fresh water than in salt or than in the air. A duck's mouth held open and the tongue pinched by a shell-fish would doubtless soon be in a feverish and abnormal condition, which cool water would tend to alleviate. One is unable to see how the ducks could have acquired the kind of human experimental knowledge attributed to them. A person might learn such a secret, but surely not a duck. In discovering and in eluding its enemies, and in many other ways, the duck's wits are very sharp, but to attribute to them a knowledge of the virtues of fresh water over salt in a certain unusual emergency — an emergency that could not have occurred to the race of ducks, much less to individuals often enough for a special instinct to have been developed to meet it — is to make them entirely human.

The whole idea of animal surgery which the incident implies — such as mending broken legs with clay, salving wounds with pitch, or resorting to bandages or amputations — is preposterous. Sick or wounded animals will often seek relief from pain by taking to the water or to the mud, or maybe to the snow, just as cows will seek the pond or the bushes to escape the heat and the flies, and that is about the extent of their surgery. The dog licks his wound; it no doubt soothes and relieves it. The cow licks her calf; she licks him into shape; it is her instinct to do so. That tongue of hers is a currycomb, plus warmth and moisture and flexibility. The cat always carries her kittens by the back of the neck; it is her best way to carry them, though I do not suppose this act is the result of experiment on her part.

A chimney swift has taken up her abode in my study chimney. At intervals, day or night, when she hears me in the room, she makes a sudden flapping and drumming sound with her wings to scare me away. It is a very pretty little trick and quite amusing. If you appear above the opening of the top of a chimney where a swift is sitting on her nest, she will try to drum you away in the same manner. I do not suppose there is any thought or calculation in her behavior, any more than there is in her nest-building, or any other of her instinctive doings. It is probably as much a reflex act as that of a bird when she turns her eggs, or feigns lameness or paralysis, to lure you away from her nest, or as the "playing possum" of a rose-bug or potato-bug when it is disturbed.

One of the writers referred to above relates with much detail this astonishing thing of the Canada lynx: He saw a pack of them trailing their game — a hare — through the winter woods, not only hunting in concert, but tracking their quarry. Now any candid and informed reader will balk at this story, for two reasons: (1) the cat tribe do not hunt by scent, but by sight, — they stalk or waylay their game; (2) they hunt singly, they are all solitary in their habits, they are probably the most unsocial of the carnivora,

—they prowl, they listen, they bide their time. Wolves often hunt in packs. I have no evidence that foxes do, and if the cats ever do, it is a most extraordinary departure. A statement of such an exceptional occurrence should always put one on his guard. In the same story the lynx is represented as making curious antics in the air to excite the curiosity of a band of caribou, and thus lure one of them to its death at the teeth and claws of the waiting hidden pack. This also is so uncatlike a proceeding that no woodsman could ever credit it. Hunters on the plains sometimes "flag" deer and antelope, and I have seen even a loon drawn very near to a bather in the water who was waving a small red flag. But none of our wild creatures use lures, or decoys, or disguises. This would involve a process of reasoning quite beyond them.

Many instances have been recorded of animals seeking the protection of man when pursued by their deadly enemies. I heard of a rat which, when hunted by a weasel, rushed into a room where a man was sleeping, and took refuge in the bed at his feet. I heard Mr. Thompson Seton tell of a young pronghorn buck that was vanquished by a rival, and so hotly pursued by its antagonist that it sought shelter amid his horses and wagons. On another occasion Mr. Seton said a jack rabbit pursued by a weasel upon the snow sought safety under his sled. In all such cases, if the frightened animal really rushed to man for protection, that act would show a degree of reason. The animal must think, and weigh the *pros* and *cons*. But I am convinced that the truth about such cases is this: The greater fear drives out the lesser fear; the animal loses its head, and becomes oblivious to everything but the enemy that is pursuing it. The rat was so terrified at the demon of a weasel that it had but one impulse, and that was to hide somewhere. Doubtless had the bed been empty, it would have taken refuge there just the same. How could an animal know that a man will protect it on special occasions, when ordinarily it has exactly the opposite feeling? A deer hotly pursued by a hound might rush into the barn-yard or into the open door of the barn in sheer desperation of uncontrollable terror. Then we should say the creature knew the farmer would protect it, and every woman who read the incident, and half the men, would believe that that thought was in the deer's mind. When the hunted deer rushes into the lake or pond, it does so, of course, with a view to escape its pursuers, and wherever it seeks refuge this is its sole purpose. I can easily fancy a bird pursued by a hawk darting into an open door or window, not with the thought that the inmates of the house will protect it, but in a panic of absolute terror. Its fear is then centred upon something behind it, not in front of it.

When an animal does something necessary to its

self-preservation, or to the continuance of its species, it probably does not think about it as a person would, any more than the plant or tree thinks about the light when it bends toward it, or about the moisture when it sends down its tap-root. Touch the tail of a porcupine ever so lightly, and it springs up like a trap and your hand is stuck with quills. I do not suppose there is any more thinking about the act, or any more conscious exercise of will-power, than there is in a trap. An outward stimulus is applied and the reaction is quick. Does not man wink, and dodge, and sneeze, and laugh, and cry, and blush, and fall in love, and do many other things without thought or will? I do not suppose the birds think about migrating, as man does when he migrates; they simply obey an inborn impulse to move south or north, as the case may be. They do not think about the great lights upon the coast that blaze out with a fatal fascination in their midnight paths. If they had independent powers of thought, they would avoid them. But the lighthouse is comparatively a new thing in the life of birds, and instinct has not yet taught them to avoid it. To adapt means to an end is an act of intelligence, but that intelligence may be inborn and instinctive as in the animals, or it may be acquired and therefore rational as in man.

"Surely," said a woman to me, "when a cat sits watching at a mouse-hole, she has some image in her mind of the mouse in its hole?" Not in any such sense as we have when we think of the same subject. The cat has either seen the mouse go into the hole, or else she smells him; she knows he is there through her senses, and she reacts to that impression. Her instinct prompts her to hunt and to catch mice; she doesn't need to think about them as we do about the game we hunt; Nature has done that for her in the shape of an inborn impulse that is awakened by the sight or smell of mice. We have no ready way to describe her act as she sits intently by the hole but to say, "The cat thinks there is a mouse there," while she is not thinking at all, but simply watching, prompted to it by her inborn instinct for mice.

The cow's mouth will water at the sight of her food when she is hungry. Is she thinking about it? No more than you are when your mouth waters as your full dinner-plate is set down before you. Certain desires and appetites are aroused through sight and smell without any mental cognition. The sexual relations of the animals also illustrate this fact.

We know that the animals do not think in any proper sense as we do, or have concepts and ideas, because they have no language. To be sure, a deaf mute thinks without language because a human being has the intelligence which language implies, or which was begotten in his ancestors by its use through long ages. Not so with the lower animals. They are like very young children in this respect; they have impressions, perceptions, emotions, but not ideas. The child perceives things, discriminates things, knows its mother from a stranger, is angry, or glad, or afraid, long before it has any language or any proper concepts. Animals know only through their senses, and this "knowledge is restricted to things present in time and space." Reflection, or a return upon themselves in thought, of this they are not capable. Their only language consists of various cries and calls, expressions of pain, alarm, joy, love, anger. They communicate with one another, and come to share one another's mental or emotional states, through these cries and calls. A dog barks in various tones and keys, each of which expresses a different feeling in the dog. I can always tell when my dog is barking at a snake; there is something peculiar in the tone. The hunter knows when his hound has driven the fox to hole by a change in his baying. The lowing and bellowing of horned cattle are expressions of several different things. The crow has many caws, that no doubt convey various meanings. The cries of alarm and distress of the birds are understood by all the wild creatures that hear them; a feeling of alarm is conveyed to them — an emotion, not an idea.

How could a crow tell his fellows of some future event, or of some experience of the day? How could he tell him this thing is dangerous, this is harmless, save by his actions in the presence of those things? Or how tell of a newly found food supply save by flying eagerly to it? A fox or a wolf could warn its fellow of the danger of poisoned meat by showing alarm in the presence of the meat. Such meat would no doubt have a peculiar odor to the keen scent of the fox or the wolf. Animals that live in communities, such as bees and beavers, coöperate with each other without language, because they form a sort of organic unity, and what one feels all the others feel. One spirit, one purpose, fills the community.

It is said on good authority that prairie-dogs will not permit weeds or tall grass to grow about their burrows, as these afford cover for coyotes and other enemies to stalk them. If they cannot remove these screens, they will leave the place. And yet they will sometimes allow a weed such as the Norse nettle or the Mexican poppy to grow on the mound at the mouth of the den where it will afford shade and not obstruct the view. At first thought this conduct may look like a matter of calculation and forethought, but it is doubtless the result of an instinct that has been developed in the tribe by the struggle for existence, and with any given rodent is quite independent of experience. It is an inherited fear of every weed or tuft of grass that might conceal an enemy.

I am told that prairie wolves will dig up and eat meat that has been poisoned and then buried, when they will not touch it if left on the surface. In such a case the ranchmen think the wolf has been outwitted; but the truth probably is that there was no calculation in the matter; the soil drew out or dulled the smell of the poison and of the man's hand, and so allayed the wolf's suspicions.

I suppose that when an animal practices deception, as when a bird feigns lameness or a broken wing to decoy you away from her nest or her young, it is quite unconscious of the act. It takes no thought about the matter. In trying to call a hen to his side, a rooster will often make believe he has food in his beak, when the pretended grain or insect may be only a pebble or a bit of stick. He picks it up and then drops it in sight of the hen, and calls her in his most persuasive manner. I do not suppose that in such cases the rooster is conscious of the fraud he is practicing. His instinct, under such circumstances, is to pick up food and call the attention of the hen to it, and when no food is present, he instinctively picks up a pebble or a stick. His main purpose is to get the hen near him, and not to feed her. When he is intent only on feeding her, he never offers her a stone instead of bread.

We have only to think of the animals as habitually in a condition analogous to, or identical with, the unthinking and involuntary character of much of our own lives. They are creatures of routine. They are wholly immersed in the unconscious, involuntary nature out of which we rise, and above which our higher lives go on.

XI

THE LITERARY TREATMENT OF NATURE

THE literary treatment of natural history themes is, of course, quite different from the scientific treatment, and should be so. The former, compared with the latter, is like free-hand drawing compared with mechanical drawing. Literature aims to give us the truth in a way to touch our emotions, and in some degree to satisfy the enjoyment we have in the living reality. The literary artist is just as much in love with the fact as is his scientific brother, only he makes a different use of the fact, and his interest in it is often of a non-scientific character. His method is synthetic rather than analytic. He deals in general, and not in technical truths, — truths that he arrives at in the fields and woods, and not in the laboratory.

The essay-naturalist observes and admires; the scientific naturalist collects. One brings home a bouquet from the woods; the other, specimens for his herbarium. The former would enlist your sympathies and arouse your enthusiasm; the latter would add to your store of exact knowledge. The one is just as shy of over-coloring or falsifying his facts as the other, only he gives more than facts, — he gives impressions and analogies, and, as far as possible, shows you the live bird on the bough.

The literary and the scientific treatment of the dog, for instance, will differ widely, not to say radically, but they will not differ in one being true and the other false. Each will be true in its own way. One will be suggestive and the other exact; one will be strictly objective, but literature is always more or less subjective. Literature aims to invest its subject with a human interest, and to this end stirs our sympathies and emotions. Pure science aims to convince the reason and the understanding alone. Note Maeterlinck's treatment of the dog in a late magazine article, probably the best thing on our four-footed comrade that English literature has to show. It gives one pleasure, not because it is all true as science is true, but because it is so tender, human, and sympathetic, without being false to the essential dog nature; it does not make the dog *do* impossible things. It is not natural history, it is literature; it is not a record of observations upon the manners and habits of the dog, but reflections upon him and his relations to man, and upon the many problems, from the human point of view, that the dog must master in a brief time: the distinctions he must figure out, the mistakes he must avoid, the riddles of life he must read in his dumb dog way. Of course, as a matter of fact, the dog is not compelled "in less than five or six weeks to get into his mind, taking shape within it, an image and a satisfactory conception of the universe." No, nor in five or six years. Strictly speaking, he is not capable of conceptions at all, but only of sense impressions; his sure guide is instinct — not blundering reason. The dog starts with a fund of knowledge, which man acquires slowly and painfully. But all this does not trouble one in reading of Maeterlinck's dog. Our interest is awakened, and our sympathies are moved, by seeing the world presented to the dog as it presents itself to us, or by putting ourselves in the dog's place. It is not false natural history, it is a fund of true human sentiment awakened by the contemplation of the dog's life and character.

Maeterlinck does not ascribe human powers and capacities to his dumb friend, the dog; he has no incredible tales of its sagacity and wit to relate; it is only an ordinary bull pup that he describes, but he makes us love it, and, through it, all other dogs, by his loving analysis of its trials and tribulations, and its devotion to its god, man. In like manner, in John Muir's story of his dog Stickeen, — a story to go with "Rab and his Friends," — our credulity is not once challenged. Our sympathies are deeply moved because our reason is not in the least outraged. It is true that Muir makes his dog act like a human being under the press of great danger; but the action is not the kind that involves reason; it only implies sense perception, and the instinct of self-preservation. Stickeen does as his master bids him, and he is human only in the human emotions of fear, despair, joy, that he shows.

In Mr. Egerton Young's book, called "My Dogs of the Northland," I find much that is interesting and several vivid dog portraits, but Mr. Young humanizes his dogs to a greater extent than does either Muir or Maeterlinck. For instance, he makes his dog Jack take special delight in teasing the Indian servant girl by walking or lying upon her kitchen floor when she had just cleaned it, all in revenge for the slights the girl had put upon him; and he gives several instances of the conduct of the dog which he thus interprets. Now one can believe almost anything of dogs in the way of wit about their food, their safety, and the like, but one cannot make them so entirely human as deliberately to plan and execute the kind of revenge here imputed to Jack. No animal could appreciate a woman's pride in a clean kitchen floor, or see any relation between the tracks which he makes upon the floor and her state of feeling toward himself. Mr. Young's facts are doubtless all right; it is his interpretation of them that is wrong.

It is perfectly legitimate for the animal story writer to put himself inside the animal he wishes to portray, and tell how life and the world look from that point of view; but he must always be true to the facts of the case, and to the limited intelligence for which he speaks.

In the humanization of the animals, and of the facts of natural history which is supposed to be the province of literature in this field, we must recognize certain limits. Your facts are sufficiently humanized the moment they become interesting, and they become interesting the moment you relate them in any way to our lives, or make them suggestive of what we know to be true in other fields and in our own experience. Thoreau made his battle of the ants interesting because he made it illustrate all the human traits of courage, fortitude, heroism, self-sacrifice. Burns's mouse at once strikes a sympathetic chord in us without ceasing to be a mouse; we see ourselves in it. To attribute human motives and faculties to the animals is to caricature them; but to put us in such relation with them that we feel their kinship, that we see their lives embosomed in the same iron necessity as our own, that we see in their minds a humbler manifestation of the same psychic power and intelligence that culminates and is conscious of itself in man, — that, I take it, is the true humanization.

We like to see ourselves in the nature around us. We want in some way to translate these facts and laws of outward nature into our own experiences; to relate our observations of bird or beast to our own lives. Unless they beget some human emotion in me, — the emotion of the beautiful, the sublime, — or appeal to my sense of the fit, the permanent, — unless what you learn in the fields and the woods corresponds in some way with what I know of my fellows, I shall not long be deeply interested in it. I do not want the animals humanized in any other sense. They all have human traits and ways; let those be brought out — their mirth, their joy, their curiosity, their cunning, their thrift, their relations, their wars, their loves — and all the springs of their actions laid bare as far as possible; but I do not expect my natural history to back up the Ten Commandments, or to be an illustration of the value of training-schools and kindergartens, or to afford a commentary upon the vanity of human wishes. Humanize your facts to the extent of making them interesting, if you have the art to do it, but leave the dog a dog, and the straddle-bug a straddle-bug.

Interpretation is a favorite word with some recent nature writers. It is claimed for the literary naturalist that he interprets natural history. The ways and doings of the wild creatures are exaggerated and misread under the plea of interpretation. Now, if by interpretation we mean an answer to the question, "What does this mean?" or, "What is the exact truth about it?" then there is but one interpretation of nature, and that is the scientific. What is the meaning of the fossils in the rocks? or of the carving and sculpturing of the landscape? or of a thousand and one other things in the organic and inorganic world about us? Science alone can answer. But if we mean by interpretation an answer to the inquiry, "What does this scene or incident suggest to you? how do you feel about it?" then we come to what is called the literary or poetic interpretation of nature, which, strictly speaking, is no interpretation of nature at all, but an interpretation of the writer or the poet himself. The poet or the essayist tells what the bird, or the tree, or the cloud means to him. It is himself, therefore, that is being interpreted. What do Ruskin's writings upon nature interpret? They interpret Ruskin — his wealth of moral and ethical ideas, and his wonderful imagination. Richard Jefferies tells us how the flower, or the bird, or the cloud is related to his subjective life and experience. It means this or that to him; it may mean something entirely different to another, because he may be bound to it by a different tie of association. The poet fills the lap of Earth with treasures not her own — the riches of his own spirit; science reveals the treasures that are her own, and arranges and appraises them.

Strictly speaking, there is not much in natural history that needs interpreting. We explain a fact, we interpret an oracle; we explain the action and relation of physical laws and forces, we interpret, as well as we can, the geologic record. Darwin sought to explain the origin of species, and to interpret many palæontological phenomena. We account for animal behavior on rational grounds of animal psychology; there is little to interpret. Natural history is not a cryptograph to be deciphered, it is a series of facts and incidents to be observed and recorded. If two wild animals, such as the beaver and the otter, are deadly enemies, there is good reason for it; and when we have found that reason, we have got hold of a fact in natural history. The robins are at enmity with the jays and the crow blackbirds and the cuckoos in the spring, and the reason is, these birds eat the robins' eggs. When we seek to interpret the actions of the animals, we are, I must repeat, in danger of running into all kinds of anthropomorphic absurdities, by reading their lives in terms of our own thinking and consciousness.

A man sees a flock of crows in a tree in a state of commotion; now they all caw, then only one master voice is heard, presently two or three crows fall upon one of their number and fell him to the ground. The spectator examines the victim and finds him dead, with his eyes pecked out. He interprets what he has seen as a court of justice; the crows were trying a criminal, and, having found him guilty, they proceeded to execute him. The curious instinct which often prompts animals to fall upon and destroy a member of the flock that is sick, or hurt, or blind, is difficult of explanation, but we may be quite sure that, whatever the reason is, the act is not the outcome of a judicial proceeding in which judge and jury and executioner all play their proper part. Wild crows will chase and maltreat a tame crow whenever they get a chance, just why, it would be hard to say. But the tame crow has evidently lost caste among them. I have what I consider good proof that a number of skunks that were wintering together in their den in the ground fell upon and killed and then partly devoured one of their number that had lost a foot in a trap.

Another man sees a fox lead a hound over a long railroad trestle, when the hound is caught and killed by a passing train. He interprets the fact as a cunning trick on the part of the fox to destroy his enemy! A captive fox, held to his kennel by a long chain, was seen to pick up an ear of corn that had fallen from a passing load, chew it up, scattering the kernels about, and then retire into his kennel. Presently a fat hen, attracted by the corn, approached the hidden fox, whereupon he rushed out and seized her. This was a shrewd trick on the part of the fox to capture a hen for his dinner! In this, and in the foregoing cases, the observer supplies something from his own mind. That is what he or she would do under like conditions. True, a fox does not eat corn; but an idle one, tied by a chain, might bite the kernels from an ear in a mere spirit of mischief and restlessness, as a dog or puppy might, and drop them upon the ground; a hen would very likely be attracted by them, when the fox would be quick to see his chance.

Some of the older entomologists believed that in a colony of ants and of bees the members recognized one another by means of some secret sign or password. In all cases a stranger from another colony is instantly detected, and a home member as instantly known. This sign or password, says Burmeister, as quoted by Lubbock, " serves to prevent any strange bee from entering into the same hive without being immediately detected and killed. It, however, sometimes happens that several hives have the same signs, when their several members rob each other with impunity. In these cases the bees whose hives suffer most alter their signs, and then can immediately detect their enemy." The same thing was thought to be true of a colony of ants. Others held that the bees and the ants knew one another individually, as men of the same town do! Would not any serious student of nature in our day know in advance of experiment that all this was childish and absurd? Lubbock showed by numerous experiments that bees and ants did not recognize their friends or their enemies by either of these methods. Just how they did do it he could not clearly settle, though it seems as if they were guided more by the sense of smell than by anything else. Maeterlinck in his "Life of the Bee" has much to say about the "spirit of the hive," and it does seem as if there were some mysterious agent or power at work there that cannot be located or defined.

This current effort to interpret nature has led one of the well-known prophets of the art to say that in this act of interpretation one "must struggle against fact and law to develop or keep his own individuality." This is certainly a curious notion, and I think an unsafe one, that the student of nature must struggle against fact and law, must ignore or override them, in order to give full swing to his own individuality. Is it himself, then, and not the truth that he is seeking to exploit? In the field of natural history we have been led to think the point at issue is not man's individuality, but correct observation — a true report of the wild life about us. Is one to give free rein to his fancy or imagination; to see animal life with his "vision," and not with his corporeal eyesight; to hear with his transcendental ear, and not through his auditory nerve? This may be all right in fiction or romance or fable, but why call the outcome natural history? Why set it down as a record of actual observation? Why penetrate the wilderness to interview Indians, trappers, guides, woodsmen, and thus seek to confirm your observations, if you have all the while been "struggling against fact and law," and do not want or need confirmation? If nature study is only to exploit your own individuality, why bother about what other people have or have not seen or heard? Why, in fact, go to the woods at all? Why not sit in your study and invent your facts to suit your fancyings?

My sole objection to the nature books that are the outcome of this proceeding is that they are put forth as veritable natural history, and thus mislead their readers. They are the result of a successful "struggle against fact and law" in a field where fact and law should be supreme. No doubt that, in the practical affairs of life, one often has a struggle with the fact. If one's bank balance gets on the negative side of the account, he must struggle to get it back where it belongs; he may even have the help of the bank's attorney to get it there. If one has a besetting sin of any kind, he has to struggle against that. Life is a struggle anyhow, and we are all strugglers — struggling to put the facts upon our side. But the only struggle the real nature student has with facts is to see them as they are, and to read them aright. He is just as zealous for the truth as is the man of science. In fact, nature study is only science out of school, happy in the fields and woods, loving the flower and the animal which it observes, and finding in them something for the sentiments and the emotions as well as for the understanding.

With the nature student, the human interest in the wild creatures — by which I mean our interest in them as living, struggling beings — dominates the scientific interest, or our interest in them merely as subjects for comparison and classification.

Gilbert White was a rare combination of the nature student and the man of science, and his book is one of the minor English classics. Richard Jefferies was a true nature lover, but his interests rarely take a scientific turn. Our Thoreau was in love with the natural, but still more in love with the supernatural; yet he prized the fact, and his books abound in delightful natural history observations. We have a host of nature students in our own day, bent on plucking out the heart of every mystery in the fields and woods. Some are dryly scientific, some are dull and prosy, some are sentimental, some are sensational, and a few are altogether admirable. Mr. Thompson Seton, as an artist and *raconteur*, ranks by far the highest in this field, but in reading his works as natural history, one has to be constantly on guard against his romantic tendencies.

The structure of animals, their colors, their ornaments, their distribution, their migrations, all have a significance that science may interpret for us if it can, but it is the business of every observer to report truthfully what he sees, and not to confound his facts with his theories.

Why does the cowbird lay its egg in another bird's

nest? Why are these parasitical birds found the world over? Who knows? Only there seems to be a parasitical principle in Nature that runs all through her works, in the vegetable as well as in the animal kingdom. Why is the porcupine so tame and stupid? Because it does not have to hunt for its game, and is self-armed against all comers. The struggle of life has not developed its wits. Why are robins so abundant? Because they are so adaptive, both as regards their food and their nesting-habits. They eat both fruit and insects, and will nest anywhere — in trees, sheds, walls, and on the ground. Why is the fox so cunning? Because the discipline of life has made him cunning. Man has probably always been after his fur; and his subsistence has not been easily obtained. If you ask me why the crow is so cunning, I shall be put to it for an adequate answer. It seems as if nobody could ever have wanted his skin or his carcass, and his diet does not compel him to outwit live game, as does that of the fox. His jet black plumage exposes him alike winter and summer. This drawback he has had to meet by added wit, but I can think of no other way in which he is handicapped. I do not know that he has any natural enemies; yet he is one of the most suspicious of the fowls of the air. Why is the Canada jay so much tamer than are other jays? They belong farther north, where they see less of man; they are birds of the wilderness; they are often, no doubt, hard put to it for food; their color does not make them conspicuous, — all these things, no doubt, tend to make them more familiar than their congeners. Why, again, the chickadee can be induced to perch upon your hand, and take food from it, more readily than can the nuthatch or the woodpecker, is a question not so easily answered. It being a lesser bird, it probably has fewer enemies than either of the others, and its fear would be less in proportion.

Why does the dog, the world over, use his nose in covering the bone he is hiding, and not his paw? Is it because his foot would leave a scent that would give his secret away, while his nose does not? He uses his paw in digging the hole for the bone, but its scent in this case would be obliterated by his subsequent procedure.

The foregoing is one way to interpret or explain natural facts. Everything has its reason. To hit upon this reason is to interpret it to the understanding. To interpret it to the emotions, or to the moral or to the æsthetic sense, that is another matter.

I would not be unjust or unsympathetic toward this current tendency to exalt the lower animals into the human sphere. I would only help my reader to see things as they are, and to stimulate him to love the animals as animals, and not as men. Nothing is gained by self-deception. The best discipline of life is that which prepares us to face the facts, no matter what they are. Such sweet companionship as one may have with a dog, simply because he is a dog and does not invade your own exclusive sphere! He is, in a way, like your youth come back to you, and taking form — all instinct and joy and adventure. You can ignore him, and he is not offended; you can reprove him, and he still loves you; you can hail him, and he bounds with joy; you can camp and tramp and ride with him, and his interest and curiosity and adventurous spirit give to the days and the nights the true holiday atmosphere. With him you are alone and not alone; you have both companionship and solitude. Who would have him more human or less canine? He divines your thought through his love, and feels your will in the glance of your eye. He is not a rational being, yet he is a very susceptible one, and touches us at so many points that we come to look upon him with a fraternal regard.

I suppose we should not care much for natural history, as I have before said, or for the study of nature generally, if we did not in some way find ourselves there; that is, something that is akin to our own feelings, methods, and intelligence. We have traveled that road, we find tokens of ourselves on every hand; we are "stuccoed with quadrupeds and birds all over," as Whitman says. The life-history of the humblest animal, if truly told, is profoundly interesting. If we could know all that befalls the slow moving turtle in the fields, or the toad that stumbles and fumbles along the roadside, our sympathies would be touched, and some spark of real knowledge imparted. We should not want the lives of those humble creatures "interpreted" after the manner of our sentimental "School of Nature Study," for that were to lose fact in fable; that were to give us a stone when we had asked for bread; we should want only a truthful record from the point of view of a wise, loving, human eye, such a record as, say, Gilbert White or Henry Thoreau might have given us. How interesting White makes his old turtle, hurrying to shelter when it rains, or seeking the shade of a cabbage leaf when the sun is too hot, or prancing about the garden on tiptoe in the spring by five in the morning, when the mating instinct begins to stir within him! Surely we may see ourselves in the old tortoise.

In fact, the problem of the essay-naturalist always is to make his subject interesting, and yet keep strictly within the bounds of truth.

It is always an artist's privilege to heighten or deepen natural effects. He may paint us a more beautiful woman, or a more beautiful horse, or a more beautiful landscape, than we ever saw; we are not deceived even though he outdo nature. We know where we stand and where he stands; we know that this is the power of art. If he is writing an animal romance like Kipling's story of the "White Seal," or like his "Jungle Book," there will be nothing equivocal about it, no mixture of fact and fiction, nothing to confuse or mislead the reader.

We know that here is the light that never was on sea or land, the light of the spirit. The facts are not falsified; they are transmuted. The aim of art is the beautiful, not *over* but *through* the true. The aim of the literary naturalist is the true, not over but through the beautiful; you shall find the exact facts in his pages, and you shall find them possessed of some of the allurement and suggestiveness that they had in the fields and woods. Only thus does his work attain to the rank of literature.

XII

A BEAVER'S REASON

ONE of our well-known natural historians thinks that there is no difference between a man's reason and a beaver's reason because, he says, when a man builds a dam, he first looks the ground over, and after due deliberation decides upon his plan, and a beaver, he avers, does the same. But the difference is obvious. Beavers, under the same conditions, build the same kind of dams and lodges; and all beavers as a rule do the same. Instinct is uniform in its workings; it runs in a groove. Reason varies endlessly and makes endless mistakes. Men build various kinds of dams and in various kinds of places, with various kinds of material and for various kinds of uses. They exercise individual judgment, they invent new ways and seek new ends, and of course often fail.

Every man has his own measure of reason, be it more or less. It is largely personal and original with him, and frequent failure is the penalty he pays for this gift.

But the individual beaver has only the inherited intelligence of his kind, with such slight addition as his experience may have given him. He learns to avoid traps, but he does not learn to improve upon his dam or lodge building, because he does not need to; they answer his purpose. If he had new and growing wants and aspirations like man, why then he would no longer be a beaver. He reacts to outward conditions, where man reflects and takes thought of things. His reason, if we prefer to call it such, is practically inerrant. It is blind, inasmuch as it is unconscious, but it is sure, inasmuch as it is adequate. It is a part of living nature in a sense that man's is not. If it makes a mistake, it is such a mistake as nature makes when, for instance, a hen produces an egg within an egg, or an egg without a yolk, or when more seeds germinate in the soil than can grow into plants.

A lower animal's intelligence, I say, compared with man's is blind. It does not grasp the subject perceived as ours does. When instinct perceives an object, it reacts to it, or not, just as the object is, or is not, related to its needs of one kind or another. In many ways an animal is like a child. What comes first in the child is simple perception and memory and association of memories, and these make up the main sum of an animal's intelligence. The child goes on developing till it reaches the power of reflection and of generalization — a stage of mentality that the animal never attains to.

All animal life is specialized; each animal is an

expert in its own line of work — the work of its tribe. Beavers do the work of beavers, they cut down trees and build dams, and all beavers do it alike and with the same degree of untaught skill. This is instinct, or unthinking nature.

Of a hot day a dog will often dig down to fresh earth to get cooler soil to lie on. Or he will go and lie in the creek. All dogs do these things. Now if the dog were seen to carry stones and sods to dam up the creek to make a deeper pool to lie in, then he would in a measure be imitating the beavers, and this, in the dog, could fairly be called an act of reason, because it is not a necessity of the conditions of his life; it would be of the nature of an afterthought.

All animals of a given species are wise in their own way, but not in the way of another species. The robin could not build the oriole's nest, nor the oriole build the robin's nor the swallow's. The cunning of the fox is not the cunning of the coon. The squirrel knows a good deal more about nuts than the rabbit does, but the rabbit would live where the squirrel would die. The muskrat and the beaver build lodges much alike, that is, with the entrance under water and an inner chamber above the water, and this because they are both water-animals with necessities much the same.

Now, the mark of reason is that it is endlessly adaptive, that it can apply itself to all kinds of problems, that it can adapt old means to new ends, or new means to old ends, and is capable of progressive development. It holds what it gets, and uses that as a fulcrum to get more. But this is not at all the way of animal instinct, which begins and ends as instinct and is non-progressive.

A large part of our own lives is instinctive and void of thought. We go instinctively toward the warmth and away from the cold. All our affections are instinctive, and do not wait upon the reason. Our affinities are as independent of our reflection as gravity is. Our inherited traits, the ties of race, the spirit of the times in which we live, the impressions of youth, of climate, of soil, of our surroundings, — all influence our acts and often determine them without any conscious exercise of judgment or reason on our part. Then habit is all-potent with us, temperament is potent, health and disease are potent. Indeed, the amount of conscious reason that an ordinary man uses in his life, compared with the great unreason or blind impulse and inborn tendency that impel him, is like his artificial lights compared with the light of day — indispensable on special occasions, but a feeble matter, after all. Reason is an artificial light in the sense that it is not one with the light of nature, and in the sense that men possess it in varying degrees. The lower animals have only a gleam of it now and then. They are wise as the plants and trees are wise, and are guided by their inborn tendencies.

A BEAVER'S REASON

Is instinct resourceful? Can it meet new conditions? Can it solve a new problem? If so, how does it differ from free intelligence or judgment? I am inclined to think that up to a certain point instinct is resourceful. Thus a Western correspondent writes: "At three different times I have pursued the common jack-rabbit from a level field, when the rabbit, coming to a furrow that ran at right angles to his course, jumped into it, and crouching down, slowly crept away to the end of the furrow, when it jumped out and ran at full speed again." This is a good example of the resourcefulness of instinct — the instinct to escape from an enemy — an old problem met by taking advantage of an unusual opportunity. To run, to double, to crouch, to hide, are probably all reflex acts with certain animals when hunted. The bird when pursued by a hawk rushes to cover in a tree or a bush, or beneath some object. Last summer I saw a bald eagle pursuing a fish hawk that held a fish in its talons. The hawk had a long start of the eagle, and began mounting upward, screaming in protest or defiance as it mounted. The pirate circled far beneath it for a few minutes, and then, seeing how he was distanced, turned back toward the ocean, so that I did not witness the little drama in the air that I had so long wished to see.

A wounded wild duck suddenly develops much cunning in escaping from the gunner — swimming under water, hiding by the shore with only the end of the bill in the air, or diving and seizing upon some object at the bottom, where it sometimes remains till life is extinct.

I once saw some farm-hands try to capture a fatted calf that had run all summer in a partly wooded field, till it had become rather wild. As the calf refused to be cornered, the farmer shot it with his rifle, but only inflicted a severe wound in the head. The calf then became as wild as a deer, and scaled fences in much the manner of the deer. When cornered, it turned and broke through the line in sheer desperation, and showed wonderful resources in eluding its pursuers. It coursed over the hills and gained the mountain, where it baffled its pursuers for two days before it was run down and caught. All such cases show the resources of instinct, the instinct of fear.

The skill of a bird in hiding its nest is very great, as is the cunning displayed in keeping the secret afterward. How careful it is not to betray the precious locality to the supposed enemy! Even the domestic turkey, when she hides her nest in the bush, if watched, approaches it by all manner of delays and indirections, and when she leaves it to feed, usually does so on the wing. I look upon these and kindred acts as exhibiting only the resourcefulness of instinct.

We are not to forget that the resourcefulness

and flexibility of instinct which all animals show, some more and some less, is not reason, though it is doubtless the first step toward it. Out of it the conscious reason and intelligence of man probably have been evolved. I do not object to hearing this variability and plasticity of instinct called the twilight of mind or rudimentary mentality. It is that, or something like that. What I object to is hearing those things in animal life ascribed to reason that can be easier accounted for on the theory of instinct.

I must differ from the ornithologist of the New York Zoölogical Park when he says in a recent paper that a bird's affection for her young is not an instinct, an uncontrollable emotion, but I quite agree with him that it does not differ, in kind at least, from the emotion of the human mother. In both cases the affection is instinctive, and not a matter of reason, or forethought, or afterthought at all. The two affections differ in this: that one is brief and transient, and the other is deep and lasting. Under stress of circumstances the bird will abandon her helpless young, while the human mother will not. When the food supply fails, the lower animal will not share the last morsel with its young; its fierce hunger makes it forget them. During the cold, wet summer of 1903 a vast number of half-fledged birds — orioles, finches, warblers — perished in the nest, probably from scarcity of insect food and the neglect of the mothers to hover them.

In interpreting the action of the animals, we so often do the thinking and reasoning ourselves which we attribute to them. Thus Mr. Beebe in the paper referred to says: "Birds have early learned to take clams or mussels in their beaks or claws at low tide and carry them out of the reach of the water, so that at the death of the mollusk, the relaxation of the adductor muscle would permit the shell to spring open and afford easy access to the inmate." No doubt the advancing tide would cause the bird to carry the shell-fish back out of the reach of the waves, where it might hope to get at its meat, but where it would be compelled to leave the shell unopened. But that the bird knew the fish would die there and that its shell would then open — it is in such particulars that the observer does the thinking.

Two other writers upon our birds have stated that pelicans will gather in flocks along the shore, and by manœuvring and beating the water with their wings, will drive the fish into the shallows, where they easily capture them. Here again the observer thinks for the observed. The pelicans see the fish and pursue them, without any plan to corner them in shoal water, but the inevitable result is that they are so cornered and captured. The fish are foolish, but the pelicans are not wise. The wisdom here attributed to them is human wisdom and not animal wisdom.

A BEAVER'S REASON

To observe the actions of the lower animals without reading our own thoughts into them is not an easy matter. Mr. Beebe thinks that when in early spring the peacock, in the Zoölogical Park, timidly erects its plumes before an unappreciative crow, it is merely practicing the art of showing off its gay plumes in anticipation of the time when it shall compete with its rivals before the females; in other words, that it is rehearsing its part. But I should say that the peacock struts before the crow or before spectators because it can't help it. The sexual instinct begins to flame up and master it. The fowl can no more control it than it can control its appetite for food. To practice beforehand is human. Animal practice takes the form of spontaneous play. The mock battles of two dogs or of other animals are not conscious practice on their part, but are play pure and simple, the same as human games, though their value as training is obvious enough.

Animals do not have general ideas; they receive impressions through their various senses, to which they respond. I recently read in manuscript a very clear and concise paper on the subject of animal thinking compared with that of man, in which the writer says: "There is a rudimentary abstraction before language. All the higher animals have general ideas of 'good-for-eating' and 'not-good-for-eating,' quite apart from any particular objects of which either of these qualities happens to be char-

acteristic." It is at this point, I think, that the
writer referred to goes wrong. The animal has no
idea at all about what is good to eat and what is not
good; it is guided entirely by its senses. It reacts
to the stimuli that reach it through the sight or
smell, usually the latter. There is no mental process
at all in the matter, not the most rudimentary;
there is simple reaction to stimuli, as strictly so as
when we sneeze on taking snuff. Man alone has
ideas of what is good to eat and what is not good.
When a fox prowls about a farmhouse, he has no
general idea that there are eatable things there, as
the essayist above referred to alleges. He is simply
following his nose; he smells something to which he
responds. We think for him when we attribute to
him general ideas of what he is likely to find at the
farmhouse. But when a man goes to a restaurant,
he follows an idea and not his nose, he compares the
different viands in his mind, and often decides beforehand what he will have. There is no agreement
in the two cases at all. If, when the bird chooses the
site for its nest, or the chipmunk or the woodchuck
the place for its hole, or the beaver the spot for its
dam, we make these animals think, compare, weigh,
we are simply putting ourselves in their place and
making them do as we would do under like conditions.

Animal life parallels human life at many points,
but it is in another plane. Something guides the

lower animals, but it is not thought; something restrains them, but it is not judgment; they are provident without prudence; they are active without industry; they are skillful without practice; they are wise without knowledge; they are rational without reason; they are deceptive without guile. They cross seas without a compass, they return home without guidance, they communicate without language, their flocks act as a unit without signals or leaders. When they are joyful, they sing or they play; when they are distressed, they moan or they cry; when they are jealous, they bite or they claw, or they strike or they gore, — and yet I do not suppose they experience the emotions of joy or sorrow, or anger or love, as we do, because these feelings in them do not involve reflection, memory, and what we call the higher nature, as with us.

The animals do not have to consult the almanac to know when to migrate or to go into winter quarters. At a certain time in the fall, I see the newts all making for the marshes; at a certain time in the spring, I see them all returning to the woods again. At one place where I walk, I see them on the railroad track wandering up and down between the rails, trying to get across. I often lend them a hand. They know when and in what direction to go, but not in the way I should know under the same circumstances. I should have to learn or be told; they know instinctively.

We marvel at what we call the wisdom of Nature, but how unlike our own! How blind, and yet in the end how sure! How wasteful, and yet how conserving! How helter-skelter she sows her seed, yet behold the forest or the flowery plain. Her springs leap out everywhere, yet how inevitably their waters find their way into streams, the streams into rivers, and the rivers to the sea. Nature is an engineer without science, and a builder without rules.

The animals follow the tides and the seasons; they find their own; the fittest and the luckiest survive; the struggle for life is sharp with them all; birds of a feather flock together; the young cowbirds reared by many different foster-parents all gather in flocks in the fall; they know their kind — at least, they are attracted by their kind.

A correspondent asks me if I do not think the minds of animals capable of improvement. Not in the strict sense. When we teach an animal anything, we make an impression upon its senses and repeat this impression over and over, till we establish a habit. We do not bring about any mental development as we do in the child; we mould and stamp its sense memory. It is like bending or compressing a vegetable growth till it takes a certain form.

The human animal sees through the trick, he comprehends it and does not need the endless repetition. When repetition has worn a path in our minds, then we, too, act automatically, or without conscious thought, as we do, for instance, in form-ing the letters when we write.

Wild animals are trained, but not educated. We multiply impressions upon them without add-ing to their store of knowledge, because they can-not evolve general ideas from these sense impres-sions. Here we reach their limitations. A bluebird or a robin will fight its reflected image in the window-pane of a darkened room day after day, and never master the delusion. It can take no step beyond the evidence of its senses — a hard step even for man to take. You may train your dog so that he will bound around you when he greets you without putting his feet upon you. But do you suppose the fond creature ever comes to know why you do not want his feet upon you? If he does, then he takes the step in general knowledge to which I have referred. Your cow, tethered by a long rope upon the lawn, learns many things about that rope and how to manage it that she did not know when she was first tied, but she can never know why she is tethered, or why she is not to crop the shrubbery, or paw up the turf, or reach the corn on the edge of the garden. This would imply general ideas or power of reflection. You might punish her until she was afraid to do any of these things, but you could never enlighten her on the subject. The rudest savage can, in a measure, be enlightened, he can be taught the reason why of things, but an animal cannot. We can make its impulses follow a rut, so to speak, but we cannot make them free and self-directing. Animals are the victims of habits inherited or acquired.

I was told of a fox that came nightly prowling about some deadfalls set for other game. The new-fallen snow each night showed the movements of the suspicious animal; it dared not approach nearer than several feet to the deadfalls. Then one day a red-shouldered hawk seized the bait in one of the traps, and was caught. That night a fox, presumably the same one, came and ate such parts of the body of the hawk as protruded from beneath the stone. Now, how did the fox know that the trap was sprung and was now harmless? Did not its act imply something more than instinct? We have the cunning and suspicion of the fox to start with; these are factors already in the problem that do not have to be accounted for. To the fox, as to the crow, anything that looks like design or a trap, anything that does not match with the haphazard look and general disarray of objects in nature, will put it on its guard. A deadfall is a contrivance that is not in keeping with the usual fortuitous disarray of sticks and stones in the fields and woods. The odor of the man's hand would also be there, and this of itself would put the fox on its guard. But a hawk or any other animal crushed by a stone, with part of its body protruding from beneath the stone, has quite a different air. It at least does not look threatening; the rock is not impending; the open jaws are closed. More than that, the smell of the man's hand would be less apparent, if not entirely absent. The fox drew no rational conclusions; its instinctive fear was allayed by the changed conditions of the trap. The hawk has not the fox's cunning, hence it fell an easy victim. I do not think that the cunning of the fox is any more akin to reason than is the power of smell of the hound that pursues him. Both are inborn, and are quite independent of experience. If a fox were deliberately to seek to elude the hound by running through a flock of sheep, or by following the bed of a shallow stream, or by taking to the public highway, then I think we should have to credit him with powers of reflection. It is true he often does all these things, but whether he does them by chance, or of set purpose, admits of doubt.

The cunning of a fox is as much a part of his inherited nature as is his fleetness of foot. All the more notable fur-bearing animals, as the fox, the beaver, the otter, have doubtless been persecuted by man and his savage ancestors for tens of thousands of years, and their suspicion of traps and lures, and their skill in eluding them, are the accumulated inheritance of ages.

In denying what we mean by thought or free intelligence to animals, an exception should un-

doubtedly be made in favor of the dog. I have elsewhere said that the dog is almost a human product;
he has been the companion of man so long, and has
been so loved by him, that he has come to partake,
in a measure at least, of his master's nature. If the
dog does not at times think, reflect, he does something so like it that I can find no other name for it.
Take so simple an incident as this, which is of common occurrence: A collie dog is going along the
street in advance of its master's team. It comes to
a point where the road forks; the dog takes, say,
the road to the left and trots along it a few rods,
and then, half turning, suddenly pauses and looks
back at the team. Has he not been struck by the
thought, "I do not know which way my master is
going: I will wait and see"? If the dog in such
cases does not reflect, what does he do? Can we find
any other word for his act? To ask a question by
word or deed involves some sort of a mental process, however rudimentary. Is there any other animal that would act as the collie did under like
circumstances?

A Western physician writes me that he has on
three different occasions seen his pointer dog behave as follows: He had pointed a flock of quail,
that would not sit to be flushed, but kept running.
Then the dog, without a word or sign from his master, made a long détour to the right or to the left
around the retreating birds, headed them off, and

then slowly advanced, facing the gunner, till he came to a point again, with the quail in a position to be flushed. After crediting the instinct and the training of the dog to the full, such an act, I think, shows a degree of independent judgment. The dog had not been trained to do that particular thing, and took the initiative of his own accord.

Many authentic stories are told of cats which seem to show that they too have profited in the way of added intelligence by their long intercourse with man. A lady writing to me from New York makes the following discriminating remarks upon the cat: —

" It seems to me that the reason which you ascribe for the semi-humanizing of the dog, his long intercourse with man, might apply in some degree to the cat. But it is necessary to be very fond of cats in order to perceive their qualities. The dog is 'up in every one's face,' so to speak ; always in evidence ; always on deck. But the cat is a shy, reserved, exclusive creature. The dog is the humble friend, follower, imitator, and slave of man. He will lick the foot that kicks him. The cat, instead, will scratch. The dog begs for notice. The cat must be loved much and courted assiduously before she will blossom out and humanize under the atmosphere of affection. The dog seems to me to have the typical qualities of the negro, the cat of the Indian. She is indifferent to man, cares nothing for him unless he wins her by special and consistent kindness, and throughout her long domestication has kept her wild independence, and ability to forage for herself when turned loose, whether in forest or city street. It is when she is much loved and petted that her intelligence manifests itself, in such quiet ways that an indifferent observer will never notice them. But she always knows who is fond of her, and which member of the family is fondest of her."

The correspondent who had the experience with his pointer dog relates this incident about his blooded mare: A drove of horses were pasturing in a forty-acre lot. The horses had paired off, as horses usually do under such circumstances. The doctor's thoroughbred mare had paired with another mare that was totally blind, and had been so since a colt. Through the field "ran a little creek which could not well be crossed by the horses except at a bridge at one end." One day when the farmer went to salt the animals, they all came galloping over the bridge and up to the gate, except the blind one; she could not find the bridge, and remained on the other side, whinnying and stamping, while the others were getting their salt a quarter of a mile away. Presently the blooded mare suddenly left her salt, made her way through the herd, and went at a flying gallop down across the bridge to the blind animal. Then she turned and came back, followed by the blind one. The doctor is convinced that his mare deliberately went back to conduct her blind companion over the bridge and down to the salt-lick. But the act may be more simply explained. How could the mare have known her companion was blind? What could any horse know about such a disability? The only thing implied in the incident is the attachment of one animal for another. The mare heard her mate calling, probably in tones of excitement or distress, and she flew back to her. Finding her all right, she turned toward the salt again and was followed by her fellow. Instinct did it all.

My own observation of the wild creatures has revealed nothing so near to human thought and reflection as is seen in the cases of the collie and pointer dogs above referred to. The nearest to them of anything I can now recall is an incident related by an English writer, Mr. Kearton. In one of his books, Mr. Kearton relates how he has frequently fooled sitting birds with wooden eggs. He put his counterfeits, painted and marked like the originals, into the nests of the song thrush, the blackbird, and the grasshopper warbler, and in no case was the imposition detected. In the warbler's nest he placed dummy eggs twice the size of her own, and the bird proceeded to brood them without the slightest sign of suspicion that they were not of her own laying.

But when Mr. Kearton tried his counterfeits

upon a ring plover, the fraud was detected. The plover hammered the shams with her bill "in the most skeptical fashion," and refused to sit down upon them. When two of the bird's own eggs were returned to the nest and left there with two wooden ones, the plover tried to throw out the shams, but failing to do this, "reluctantly sat down and covered good and bad alike."

Now, can the action of the plover in this case be explained on the theory of instinct alone? The bird could hardly have had such an experience before. It was offered a counterfeit, and it behaved much as you or I would have done under like conditions, although we have the general idea of counterfeits, which the plover could not have had. Of course, everything that pertains to the nest and eggs of a bird is very vital to it. The bird is wise about these things from instinct. Yet the other birds were easily fooled. We do not know how nearly perfect Mr. Kearton's imitation eggs were, but evidently there was some defect in them which arrested the bird's attention. If the incident does not show powers of reflection in the bird, it certainly shows keen powers of perception; and that birds, and indeed all animals, show varying degrees of this power, is a matter of common observation. I hesitate, therefore, to say that Mr. Kearton's plover showed anything more than very keen instincts. Among our own birds there is only one, so far as I know, that detects the egg of the cowbird when it is laid in the bird's nest, and that is the yellow warbler. All the other birds accept it as their own, but this warbler detects the imposition, and proceeds to get rid of the strange egg by burying it under a new nest bottom.

Man is undoubtedly of animal origin. The road by which he has come out of the dim past lies through the lower animals. The germ and potentiality of all that he has become or can become was sleeping there in his humble origins. Of this I have no doubt. Yet I think we are justified in saying that the difference between animal intelligence and human reason is one of kind and not merely of degree. Flying and walking are both modes of locomotion, and yet may we not fairly say they differ in kind? Reason and instinct are both manifestations of intelligence, yet do they not belong to different planes? Intensify animal instinct ever so much, and you have not reached the plane of reason. The homing instinct of certain animals is far beyond any gift of the kind possessed by man, and yet it seems in no way akin to reason. Reason heeds the points of the compass and takes note of the topography of the country, but what can animals know of these things?

And yet I say the animal is father of the man. Without the lower orders, there could have been no higher. In my opinion, no miracle or special creation is required to account for man. The transformation of force, as of heat into light or electricity, is as great a leap and as mysterious as the transformation of animal intelligence into human reason.

XIII

READING THE BOOK OF NATURE

IN studying Nature, the important thing is not so much what we see as how we interpret what we see. Do we get at the true meaning of the facts? Do we draw the right inference? The fossils in the rocks were long observed before men drew the right inference from them. So with a hundred other things in nature and life.

During May and a part of June of 1903, a drouth of unusual severity prevailed throughout the land. The pools and marshes nearly all dried up. Late in June the rains came again and filled them up. Then an unusual thing happened: suddenly, for two or three days and nights, the marshes about me were again vocal with the many voices of the hyla, the "peepers" of early spring. That is the fact. Now, what is the interpretation? With me the peepers become silent in early May, and, I suppose, leave the marshes for their life in the woods. Did the drouth destroy all their eggs and young, and did they know this and so come back to try again? How else shall one explain their second appearance in the marshes? But how did they know of the de-

231

struction of their young, and how can we account for their concerted action? These are difficulties not easily overcome. A more rational explanation to me is this, namely, that the extreme dryness of the woods — nearly two months without rain — drove the little frogs to seek for moisture in their spring haunts, where in places a little water would be pretty certain to be found. Here they were holding out, probably hibernating again, as such creatures do in the tropics during the dry season, when the rains came, and here again they sent up their spring chorus of voices, and, for aught I know, once more deposited their eggs. This to me is much more like the ways of Nature with her creatures than is the theory of the frogs' voluntary return to the swamps and pools to start the season over again.

The birds at least show little or no wit when a new problem is presented to them. They have no power of initiative. Instinct runs in a groove, and cannot take a step outside of it. One May day we started a meadowlark from her nest. There were three just hatched young in the nest, and one egg lying on the ground about two inches from the nest. I suspected that this egg was infertile and that the bird had had the sense to throw it out, but on examination it was found to contain a nearly grown bird. The inference was, then, that the egg had been accidentally carried out of the nest some time when the sitting bird had taken a sudden flight, and that she did not have the sense to roll or carry it back to its place.

There is another view of the case which no doubt the sentimental "School of Nature Study" would eagerly adopt: A very severe drouth reigned throughout the land; food was probably scarce, and was becoming scarcer ; the bird foresaw her inability to care for four young ones, and so reduced the possible number by ejecting one of the eggs from the nest. This sounds pretty and plausible, and so credits the bird with the wisdom that the public is so fond of believing it possesses. Something like this wisdom often occurs among the hive bees in seasons of scarcity ; they will destroy the unhatched queens. But birds have no such foresight, and make no such calculations. In cold, backward seasons, I think, birds lay fewer eggs than when the season is early and warm, but that is not a matter of calculation on their part; it is the result of outward conditions.

A great many observers and nature students at the present time are possessed of the notion that the birds and beasts instruct their young, train them and tutor them, much after the human manner. In the familiar sight of a pair of crows foraging with their young about a field in summer, one of our nature writers sees the old birds giving their young a lesson in flying. She says that the most important thing that the elders had to do was to teach the youngsters how to fly. This they did by circling about the pasture, giving a peculiar call while they were followed by their flock — all but one. This was a bobtailed crow, and he did not obey the word of command. His mother took note of his disobedience and proceeded to discipline him. He stood upon a big stone, and she came down upon him and knocked him off his perch. "He squawked and fluttered his wings to keep from falling, but the blow came so suddenly that he had not time to save himself, and he fell flat on the ground. In a minute he clambered back upon his stone, and I watched him closely. The next time the call came to fly he did not linger, but went with the rest, and so long as I could watch him he never disobeyed again." I should interpret this fact of the old and young crows flying about a field in summer quite differently. The young are fully fledged, and are already strong flyers, when this occurs. They do not leave the nest until they can fly well and need no tutoring. What the writer really saw was what any one may see on the farm in June and July: she saw the parent crows foraging with their young in a field The old birds flew about, followed by their brood, clamorous for the food which their parents found. The bobtailed bird, which had probably met with some accident, did not follow, and the mother returned to feed it; the young crow lifted its wings and flapped them, and in its eagerness probably fell off its perch ; then when its parent flew away, it followed.

I think it highly probable that the sense or faculty by which animals find their way home over long stretches of country, and which keeps them from ever being lost as man so often is, is a faculty entirely unlike anything man now possesses. The same may be said of the faculty that guides the birds back a thousand miles or more to their old breeding-haunts. In caged or housed animals I fancy this faculty soon becomes blunted. President Roosevelt tells in his "Ranch Life" of a horse he owned that ran away two hundred miles across the plains, swimming rivers on the way to its old home. It is very certain, I think, that this homing feat is not accomplished by the aid of either sight or scent, for usually the returning animal seems to follow a comparatively straight line. It is, or seems to be, a consciousness of direction that is as unerring as the magnetic needle. Reason, calculation, and judgment err, but these primary instincts of the animal seem almost infallible.

In Bronx Park in New York a grebe and a loon lived together in an inclosure in which was a large pool of water. The two birds became much attached to each other and were never long separated. One winter day on which the pool was frozen over, except a small opening in one end of it, the grebe dived under the ice and made its way to the far end of the pool, where it remained swimming about aimlessly for some moments. Presently the loon missed its companion, and with an apparent look of concern dived under the ice and joined it at the closed end of the pool. The grebe seemed to be in distress for want of air. Then the loon settled upon the bottom, and with lifted beak sprang up with much force against the ice, piercing it with its dagger-like bill, but not breaking it. Down to the bottom it went again, and again hurled itself up against the ice, this time shattering it and rising to the surface, where the grebe was quick to follow. Now it looked as if the loon had gone under the ice to rescue its friend from a dangerous situation, for had not the grebe soon found the air, it must have perished, and persons who witnessed the incident interpreted it in this way. It is in such cases that we are so apt to read our human motives and emotions into the acts of the lower animals. I do not suppose the loon realized the danger of its companion, nor went under the ice to rescue it. It followed the grebe because it wanted to be with it, or to share in any food that might be detaining it there, and then, finding no air-hole, it proceeded to make one, as it and its ancestors must often have done before. All our northern divers must be more or less acquainted with ice, and must know how to break it. The grebe itself could doubtless have broken the ice had it desired to. The birds and the beasts often show much intelligence, or what looks like intelligence, but, as Hamerton says, "the moment we think of them as *human*, we are lost."

A farmer had a yearling that sucked the cows. To prevent this, he put on the yearling a muzzle set full of sharpened nails. These of course pricked the cows, and they would not stand to be drained of their milk. The next day the farmer saw the yearling rubbing the nails against a rock in order, as he thought, to dull them so they would not prick the cows! How much easier to believe that the beast was simply trying to get rid of the awkward incumbrance upon its nose. What can a calf or a cow know about sharpened nails, and the use of a rock to dull them? This is a kind of outside knowledge — outside of their needs and experiences — that they could not possess.

An Arizona friend of mine lately told me this interesting incident about the gophers that infested his cabin when he was a miner. The gophers ate up his bread. He could not hide it from them or put it beyond their reach. Finally, he bethought him to stick his loaf on the end of a long iron poker that he had, and then stand up the poker in the middle of his floor. Still, when he came back to his cabin, he would find his loaf eaten full of holes. One day, having nothing to do, he concluded to watch and see how the gophers reached the bread, and this was what he saw: The animals climbed up the side of his log cabin, ran along one of the logs to a point opposite the bread, and then sprang out sidewise toward the loaf, which each one struck, but upon which only one seemed able to effect a lodgment. Then this one would cling to the loaf and act as a stop to his fellows when they tried a second time, his body affording them the barrier they required. My friend felt sure that this leader deliberately and consciously aided the others in securing a footing on the loaf. But I read the incident differently. This successful jumper aided his fellows without designing it. The exigencies of the situation compelled him to the course he pursued. Having effected a lodgment upon the impaled loaf, he would of course cling to it when the others jumped so as not to be dislodged, thereby, willy nilly, helping them to secure a foothold. The coöperation was inevitable, and not the result of design.

The power to see straight is the rarest of gifts; to see no more and no less than is actually before you; to be able to detach yourself and see the thing as it actually is, uncolored or unmodified by your own sentiments or prepossessions. In short, to see with your reason as well as with your perceptions, that is to be an observer and to read the book of nature aright.

XIV

GATHERED BY THE WAY

I. THE TRAINING OF WILD ANIMALS

I WAS reminded afresh of how prone we all are to regard the actions of the lower animals in the light of our own psychology on reading "The Training of Wild Animals," by Bostock, a well-known animal-trainer. Bostock evidently knows well the art of training animals, but of the science of it he seems to know very little. That is, while he is a successful trainer, his notions of animal psychology are very crude. For instance, on one page he speaks of the lion as if it were endowed with a fair measure of human intelligence, and had notions, feelings, and thoughts like our own; on the next page, when he gets down to real business, he lays bare its utter want of these things. He says a lion born and bred in captivity is more difficult to train than one caught from the jungle. Then he gives rein to his fancy. "Such a lion does not fear man; he knows his own power. He regards man as an inferior, with an attitude of disdain and silent hauteur." "He accepts his food as tribute, and his care as homage due." "He is aristocratic in his independence."

"Deep in him — so deep that he barely realizes its existence — slumbers a desire for freedom and an unutterable longing for the blue sky and the free air." When his training is begun, "he meets it with a reserved majesty and silent indifference, as though he had a dumb realization of his wrongs." All this is a very human way of looking at the matter, and is typical of the way we all — most of us — speak of the lower animals, defining them to ourselves in terms of our own mentality, but it leads to false notions about them. We look upon an animal fretting and struggling in its cage as longing for freedom, picturing to itself the joy of the open air and the free hills and sky, when the truth of the matter undoubtedly is that the fluttering bird or restless fox or lion simply feels discomfort in confinement. Its sufferings are physical, and not mental. Its instincts lead it to struggle for freedom. It reacts strongly against the barriers that hold it, and tries in every way to overcome them. Freedom, as an idea, or a conception of a condition of life, is, of course, beyond its capacity.

Bostock shows how the animal learns entirely by association, and not at all by the exercise of thought or reason, and yet a moment later says: "The animal is becoming amenable to the mastery of man, and in doing so his own reason is being developed," which is much like saying that when a man is practicing on the flying trapeze his wings are being de-

veloped. The lion learns slowly through association
—through repeated sense impressions. First a long
stick is put into his cage. If this is destroyed, it is
replaced by another, until he gets used to it and tolerates its presence. Then he is gently rubbed with
it at the hands of his keeper. He gets used to this
and comes to like it. Then the stick is baited with
a piece of meat, and in taking the meat the animal
gets still better acquainted with the stick, and so
ceases to fear it. When this stage is reached, the
stick is shortened day by day, "until finally it is not
much longer than the hand." The next step is to let
the hand take the place of the stick in the stroking
process. "This is a great step taken, for one of the
most difficult things is to get any wild animal to allow
himself to be touched with the human hand." After a
time a collar with a chain attached is slipped around
the lion's neck when he is asleep. He is now chained
to one end of the cage. Then a chair is introduced
into the cage; whereupon this king of beasts, whose
reason is being developed, and who has such clear
notions of inferior and superior, and who knows his
own powers, usually springs for the chair, seeking to
demolish it. His tether prevents his reaching it, and
so in time he tolerates the chair. Then the trainer,
after some preliminary feints, walks into the cage
and seats himself in the chair. And so, inch by inch,
as it were, the trainer gets control of the animal
and subdues him to his purposes, not by appealing

to his mind, for he has none, but by impressions upon his senses.

"Leopards, panthers, and jaguars are all trained in much the same manner," and in putting them through their tricks one invariable order must be observed: "Each thing done one day must be done the next day in exactly the same way; there must be no deviation from the rule." Now we do not see in this fact the way of a thinking or reflecting being, but rather the way of a creature governed by instinct or unthinking intelligence. An animal never *learns* a trick in the sense that man learns it, never sees through it or comprehends it, has no image of it in its mind, and no idea of the relations of the parts of it to one another; it does it by reason of repetition, as a creek wears its channel, and probably has no more self-knowledge or self-thought than the creek has. This, I think, is quite contrary to the popular notion of animal life and mentality, but it is the conclusion that I, at least, cannot avoid after making a study of the subject.

II. AN ASTONISHED PORCUPINE

One summer, while three young people and I were spending an afternoon upon a mountain-top, our dogs treed a porcupine. At my suggestion the young man climbed the tree — not a large one — to shake the animal down. I wished to see what the dogs would do with him, and what the "quill-pig" would do with the dogs. As the climber advanced the rodent went higher, till the limb he clung to was no larger than one's wrist. This the young man seized and shook vigorously. I expected to see the slow, stupid porcupine drop, but he did not. He only tightened his hold. The climber tightened his hold, too, and shook the harder. Still the bundle of quills did not come down, and no amount of shaking could bring it down. Then I handed a long pole up to the climber, and he tried to punch the animal down. This attack in the rear was evidently a surprise; it produced an impression different from that of the shaking. The porcupine struck the pole with his tail, put up the shield of quills upon his back, and assumed his best attitude of defense. Still the pole persisted in its persecution, regardless of the quills; evidently the animal was astonished: he had never had an experience like this before; he had now met a foe that despised his terrible quills. Then he began to back rapidly down the tree in the face of his enemy. The young man's sweetheart stood below, a highly interested spectator. "Look out, Sam, he's coming down!" "Be quick, he's gaining on you!" "Hurry, Sam!" Sam came as fast as he could, but he had to look out for his footing, and his antagonist did not. Still, he reached the ground first, and his sweetheart breathed more easily. It looked as if the porcupine reasoned thus: "My quills are useless against a foe so far away;

I must come to close quarters with him." But, of course, the stupid creature had no such mental process, and formed no such purpose. He had found the tree unsafe, and his instinct now was to get to the ground as quickly as possible and take refuge among the rocks. As he came down I hit him a slight blow over the nose with a rotten stick, hoping only to confuse him a little, but much to my surprise and mortification he dropped to the ground and rolled down the hill dead, having succumbed to a blow that a woodchuck or a coon would hardly have regarded at all. Thus does the easy, passive mode of defense of the porcupine not only dull his wits, but it makes frail and brittle the thread of his life. He has had no struggles or battles to harden and toughen him.

That blunt nose of his is as tender as a baby's, and he is snuffed out by a blow that would hardly bewilder for a moment any other forest animal, unless it be the skunk, another sluggish non-combatant of our woodlands. Immunity from foes, from effort, from struggle is always purchased with a price.

Certain of our natural history romancers have taken liberties with the porcupine in one respect: they have shown him made up into a ball and rolling down a hill. One writer makes him do this in a sportive mood; he rolls down a long hill in the woods, and at the bottom he is a ragged mass of leaves which his quills have impaled — an apparition that nearly frightened a rabbit out of its wits.

Dog and Porcupine

Let any one who knows the porcupine try to fancy it performing a feat like this!

Another romancer makes his porcupine roll himself into a ball when attacked by a panther, and then on a nudge from his enemy roll down a snowy incline into the water. I believe the little European hedgehog can roll itself up into something like a ball, but our porcupine does not. I have tried all sorts of tricks with him, and made all sorts of assaults upon him, at different times, and I have never yet seen him assume the globular form. It would not be the best form for him to assume, because it would partly expose his vulnerable under side. The one thing the porcupine seems bent upon doing at all times is to keep right side up with care. His attitude of defense is crouching close to the ground, head drawn in and pressed down, the circular shield of large quills upon his back opened and extended as far as possible, and the tail stretched back rigid and held close upon the ground. "Now come on," he says, "if you want to." The tail is his weapon of active defense; with it he strikes upward like lightning, and drives the quills into whatever they touch. In his chapter called "In Panoply of Spears," Mr. Roberts paints the porcupine without taking any liberties with the creature's known habits. He portrays one characteristic of the porcupine very felicitously: "As the porcupine made his resolute way through the woods, the manner of his going differed from that of all the other kindreds of the wild. He went not furtively. He had no particular objection to making a noise. He did not consider it necessary to stop every little while, stiffen himself to a monument of immobility, cast wary glances about the gloom, and sniff the air for the taint of enemies. He did not care who knew of his coming, and he did not greatly care who came. Behind his panoply of biting spears he felt himself secure, and in that security he moved as if he held in fee the whole green, shadowy, perilous woodland world."

III. BIRDS AND STRINGS

A college professor writes me as follows: —

"Watching this morning a robin attempting to carry off a string, one end of which was caught in a tree, I was much impressed by his utter lack of sense. He could not realize that the string was fast, or that it must be loosened before it could be carried off, and in his efforts to get it all in his bill he wound it about a neighboring limb. If as little sense were displayed in using other material for nests, there would be no robins' nests. It impressed me more than ever with the important part played by instinct."

Who ever saw any of our common birds display any sense or judgment in the handling of strings? Strings are comparatively a new thing with birds; they are not a natural product, and as a matter of course birds blunder in handling them. The oriole uses them the most successfully, often attaching her pensile nest to the branch by their aid. But she uses them in a blind, childish way, winding them round and round the branch, often getting them looped over a twig or hopelessly tangled, and now and then hanging herself with them, as is the case with other birds. I have seen a sparrow, a cedar-bird, and a robin each hung by a string it was using in the building of its nest. Last spring, in Spokane, a boy brought me a desiccated robin, whose feet were held together by a long thread hopelessly snarled. The boy had found it hanging to a tree.

I have seen in a bird magazine a photograph of an oriole's nest that had a string carried around a branch apparently a foot or more away, and then brought back and the end woven into the nest. It was given as a sample of a well-guyed nest, the discoverer no doubt looking upon it as proof of an oriole's forethought in providing against winds and storms. I have seen an oriole's nest with a string carried around a leaf, and another with a long looped string hanging free. All such cases simply show that the bird was not master of her material; she bungled; the trailing string caught over the leaf or branch, and she drew both ends in and fastened them regardless of what had happened. The incident only shows how blindly instinct works.

Twice I have seen cedar-birds, in their quest for

nesting-material, trying to carry away the strings that orioles had attached to branches. According to our sentimental "School of Nature Study," the birds should have untied and unsnarled the strings in a human way, but they did not; they simply tugged at them, bringing their weight to bear, and tried to fly away with the loose end.

In view of the ignorance of birds with regard to strings, how can we credit the story told by one of our popular nature writers of a pair of orioles that deliberately impaled a piece of cloth upon a thorn in order that it might be held firmly while they pulled out the threads? When it came loose, they refastened it. The story is incredible for two reasons: (1) the male oriole does not assist the female in building the nest; he only furnishes the music; (2) the whole proceeding implies an amount of reflection and skill in dealing with a new problem that none of our birds possess. What experience has the race of orioles had with cloth, that any member of it should know how to unravel it in that way? The whole idea is absurd.

IV. MIMICRY

To what lengths the protective resemblance theory is pushed by some of its expounders! Thus, in the neighborhood of Rio Janeiro there are two species of hawks that closely resemble each other, but one eats only insects and the other eats birds.

Mr. Wallace thinks that the bird-eater mimics the insect-eater, so as to deceive the birds, which are not afraid of the latter. But if the two hawks look alike, would not the birds come to regard them both as bird-eaters, since one of them does eat birds? Would they not at once identify the harmless one with their real enemy and thus fear them both alike? If the latter were newcomers and vastly in the minority, then the ruse might work for a while. But if there were ten harmless hawks around to one dangerous one, the former would quickly suffer from the character of the latter in the estimation of the birds. Birds are instinctively afraid of all hawk kind.

Wallace thinks it may be an advantage to cuckoos, a rather feeble class of birds, to resemble the hawks, but this seems to me far-fetched. True it is, if the sheep could imitate the wolf, its enemies might keep clear of it. Why, then, has not this resemblance been brought about? Our cuckoo is a feeble and defenseless bird also, but it bears no resemblance to the hawk. The same can be said of scores of other birds.

Many of these close resemblances among different species of animals are no doubt purely accidental, or the result of the same law of variation acting under similar conditions. We have a hummingbird moth that so closely in its form and flight and manner resembles a hummingbird, that if this resemblance brought it any immunity from danger it would be set down as a clear case of mimicry. There is such a moth in England, too, where no humming-bird is found. Why should not Nature repeat herself in this way? This moth feeds upon the nectar of flowers like the hummingbird, and why should it not have the hummingbird's form and manner?

Then there are accidental resemblances in nature, such as the often-seen resemblance of knots of trees and of vegetables to the human form, and of a cer-tain fungus to a part of man's anatomy. We have a fly that resembles a honey-bee. In my bee-hunting days I used to call it the "mock honey-bee." It would come up the wind on the scent of my bee box and hum about it precisely like a real bee. Of course it was here before the honey-bee, and has been evolved quite independently of it. It feeds upon the pollen and nectar of flowers like the true bee, and is, therefore, of similar form and color. The honey-bee has its enemies; the toads and tree-frogs feed upon it, and the kingbird captures the slow drone.

When an edible butterfly mimics an inedible or noxious one, as is frequently the case in the tropics, the mimicker is no doubt the gainer.

It makes a big difference whether the mimicker is seeking to escape from an enemy, or seeking to deceive its prey. I fail to see how, in the latter case, any disguise of form or color could be brought about.

Our shrike, at times, murders little birds and eats out their brains, and it has not the form, or the color, or the eye of a bird of prey, and thus probably deceives its victims, but there is no reason to believe that this guise is the result of any sort of mimicry.

V. THE COLORS OF FRUITS

Mr. Wallace even looks upon the nuts as protectively colored, because they are not to be eaten. But without the agency of the birds and the squirrels, how are the heavy nuts, such as the chestnut, beechnut, acorn, butternut, and the like, to be scattered? The blue jay is often busy hours at a time in the fall, planting chestnuts and acorns, and red squirrels carry butternuts and walnuts far from the parent trees, and place them in forked limbs and holes for future use. Of course, many of these fall to the ground and take root. If the protective coloration of the nuts, then, were effective, it would defeat a purpose which every tree and shrub and plant has at heart, namely, the scattering of its seed. I notice that the button-balls on the sycamores are protectively colored also, and certainly they do not crave concealment. It is true that they hang on the naked trees till spring, when no concealment is possible. It is also true that the jays and the crows carry away the chestnuts from the open burrs on the trees where no color scheme would conceal them. But the squirrels find them upon the ground even beneath the snow, being guided, no doubt, by the sense of smell.

The hickory nut is almost white; why does it not

seek concealment also? It is just as helpless as the others, and is just as sweet-meated. It occurs to me that birds can do nothing with it on account of its thick shell; it needs, therefore, to attract some four-footed creature that will carry it away from the parent tree, and this is done by the mice and the squirrels. But if this is the reason of its whiteness, there is the dusky butternut and the black walnut, both more or less concealed by their color, and yet having the same need of some creature to scatter them.

The seeds of the maple, and of the ash and the linden, are obscurely colored, and they are winged; hence they do not need the aid of any creature in their dissemination. To say that this is the reason of their dull, unattractive tints would be an explanation on a par with much that one hears about the significance of animal and vegetable coloration. Why is corn so bright colored, and wheat and barley so dull, and rice so white? No doubt there is a reason in each case, but I doubt if that reason has any relation to the surrounding animal life.

The new Botany teaches that the flowers have color and perfume to attract the insects to aid in their fertilization — a need so paramount with all plants, because plants that are fertilized by aid of the wind have very inconspicuous flowers. Is it equally true that the high color of most fruits is to attract some hungry creature to come and eat them and thus scatter the seeds? From the dwarf cornel, or bunch-berry, in the woods, to the red thorn in the fields, every fruit-bearing plant and shrub and tree seems to advertise itself to the passer-by in its bright hues. Apparently there is no other use to the plant of the fleshy pericarp than to serve as a bait or wage for some animal to come and sow its seed. Why, then, should it not take on these alluring colors to help along this end? And yet there comes the thought, may not this scarlet and gold of the berries and tree fruits be the inevitable result of the chemistry of ripening, as it is with the autumn foliage? What benefit to the tree, directly or indirectly, is all this wealth of color of the autumn? Many of the toadstools are highly colored also; how do they profit by it? Many of the shells upon the beach are very showy; to what end? The cherry-birds find the pale ox-hearts as readily as they do the brilliant Murillos, and the dull blue cedar berries and the duller drupes of the lotus are not concealed from them nor from the robins. But it is true that the greenish white grapes in the vineyard do not suffer from the attacks of the birds as do the blue and red ones. The reason probably is that the birds regard them as unripe. The white grape is quite recent, and the birds have not yet "caught on."

Poisonous fruits are also highly colored; to what end? In Bermuda I saw on low bushes great masses of what they called "pigeon-berries" of a brilliant yellow color and very tempting, yet I was assured they were poisonous. It would be interesting to know if anything eats the red berries of our wild turnip or arum. I doubt if any bird or beast could stand them. Wherefore, then, are they so brightly colored? I am also equally curious to know if anything eats the fruit of the red and white baneberry and the blue cohosh.

The seeds of some wild fruit, such as the climbing bitter-sweet, are so soft that it seems impossible they should pass through the gizzard of a bird and not be destroyed.

The fruit of the sumac comes the nearest to being a cheat of anything I know of in nature — a collection of seeds covered with a flannel coat with just a perceptible acid taste, and all highly colored. Unless the seed itself is digested, what is there to tempt the bird to devour it, or to reward it for so doing?

In the tropics one sees fruits that do not become bright colored on ripening, such as the breadfruit, the custard apple, the naseberry, the mango. And tropical foliage never colors up as does the foliage of northern trees.

VI. INSTINCT

Many false notions seem to be current in the popular mind about instinct. Apparently, some of our writers on natural history themes would like to discard the word entirely. Now instinct is not opposed to intelligence; it is intelligence of the unlearned, unconscious kind, —the intelligence innate in nature. We use the word to distinguish a gift or faculty which animals possess, and which is independent of instruction and experience, from the mental equipment of man which depends mainly upon instruction and experience. A man has to be taught to do that which the lower animals do from nature. Hence the animals do not progress in knowledge, while man's progress is almost limitless. A man is an animal born again into a higher spiritual plane. He has lost or shed many of his animal instincts in the process, but he has gained the capacity for great and wonderful improvement.

Instinct is opposed to reason, to reflection, to thought, —to that kind of intelligence which knows and takes cognizance of itself. Instinct is that lower form of intelligence which acts through the senses, — sense perception, sense association, sense memory, — which we share with the animals, though their eyes and ears and noses are often quicker and keener than ours. Hence the animals know only the present, visible, objective world, while man through his gift of reason and thought knows the inward world of ideas and ideal relations.

An animal for the most part knows all that it is necessary for it to know as soon as it reaches maturity; what it learns beyond that, what it learns at the hands of the animal-trainer, for instance, it learns slowly, through a long repetition of the pro-

cess of trial and failure. Man also achieves many
things through practice alone, or through the same
process of trial and failure. Much of his manual
skill comes in this way, but he learns certain things
through the exercise of his reason; he sees how the
thing is done, and the relation of the elements of the
problem to one another. The trained animal never
sees *how* the thing is done, it simply does it automatically, because certain sense impressions have
been stamped upon it till a habit has been formed,
just as a man will often wind his watch before going
to bed, or do some other accustomed act, without
thinking of it.

The bird builds her nest and builds it intelligently, that is, she adapts means to an end; but
there is no reason to suppose that she *thinks* about
it in the sense that man does when he builds his
house. The nest-building instinct is stimulated into
activity by outward conditions of place and climate
and food supply as truly as the growth of a plant is
thus stimulated.

As I look upon the matter, the most wonderful
and ingenious nests in the world, as those of the
weaver-birds and orioles, show no more independent
self-directed and self-originated thought than does
the rude nest of the pigeon or the cuckoo. They
evince a higher grade of intelligent instinct, and that
is all. Both are equally the result of natural promptings, and not of acquired skill, or the lack of it One

species of bird will occasionally learn the song of another species, but the song impulse must be there to begin with, and this must be stimulated in the right way at the right time. A caged English sparrow has been known to learn the song of the canary caged with or near it, but the sparrow certainly inherits the song impulse. One has proof of this when he hears a company of these sparrows sitting in a tree in spring chattering and chirping in unison, and almost reaching an utterance that is song-like. Our cedar-bird does not seem to have the song impulse, and I doubt if it could ever be taught to sing. In like manner our ruffed grouse has but feeble vocal powers, and I do not suppose it would learn to crow or cackle if brought up in the barn-yard. It expresses its joy at the return of spring and the mating season in its drum, as do the woodpeckers.

The recent English writer Richard Kearton says there is "no such dead level of unreasoning instinct" in the animal world as is popularly supposed, and he seems to base the remark upon the fact that he found certain of the cavities or holes in a hay-rick where sparrows roosted lined with feathers, while others were not lined. Such departures from a level line of habit as this are common enough among all creatures. Instinct is not something as rigid as cast iron; it does not invariably act like a machine, always the same. The animal is something alive, and is subject to the law of variation. Instinct may act more strongly in one kind than in another, just as reason may act more strongly in one man than in another, or as one animal may have greater speed or courage than another of the same species. It would be hard to find two live creatures, very far up in the scale, exactly alike. A thrush may use much mud in the construction of its nest, or it may use little or none at all; the oriole may weave strings into its nest, or it may use only dry grasses and horse-hairs ; such cases only show variations in the action of instinct. But if an oriole should build a nest like a robin, or a robin build like a cliff swallow, that would be a departure from instinct to take note of.

Some birds show a much higher degree of variability than others; some species vary much in song, others in nesting and in feeding habits. I have never noticed much variation in the songs of robins, but in their nesting-habits they vary constantly. Thus one nest will be almost destitute of mud, while another will be composed almost mainly of mud; one will have a large mass of dry grass and weeds as its foundation, while the next one will have little or no foundation of the kind. The sites chosen vary still more, ranging from the ground all the way to the tops of trees. I have seen a robin's nest built in the centre of a small box that held a clump of ferns, which stood by the roadside on the top of a low post near a house, and without cover or shield of any sort. The robin had welded her nest so completely to the soil in the box that the whole could be lifted by the rim of the nest. She had given a very pretty and unique effect to the nest by a border of fine dark rootlets skillfully woven together. The song sparrow shows a high degree of variability both in its song and in its nesting-habits, each bird having several songs of its own, while one may nest upon the ground and another in a low bush, or in the vines on the side of your house. The vesper sparrow, on the other hand, shows a much lower degree of variability, the individuals rarely differing in their songs, while all the nests I have ever found of this sparrow were in open grassy fields upon the ground. The chipping or social sparrow is usually very constant in its song and its nesting-habits, and yet one season a chippy built her nest in an old robin's nest in the vines on my porch. It was a very pretty instance of adaptation on the part of the little bird. Another chippy that I knew had an original song, one that resembled the sound of a small tin whistle. The bush sparrow, too, is pretty constant in choosing a bush in which to place its nest, yet I once found the nest of this sparrow upon the ground in an open field with suitable bushes within a few yards of it. The woodpeckers, the jays, the cuckoos, the pewees, the warblers, and other wood birds show only a low degree of variability in song, feeding, and nesting habits.

The Baltimore oriole makes free use of strings in its nest-building, and the songs of different birds of this species vary greatly, while the orchard oriole makes no use of strings, so far as I have observed, and its song is always and everywhere the same. Hence we may say that the lives of some birds run much more in ruts than do those of others; they show less plasticity of instinct, and are perhaps for that reason less near the state of free intelligence.

Organic life in all its forms is flexible; instinct is flexible; the habits of all the animals change more or less with changed conditions, but the range of the fluctuations in the lives of the wild creatures is very limited, and is always determined by surrounding circumstances, and not by individual volition, as it so often is in the case of man. In a treeless country birds that sing on the perch elsewhere will sing on the wing. The black bear in the Southern States "holes up" for a much shorter period than in Canada or the Rockies. Why is the spruce grouse so stupid compared with most other species? Why is the Canada jay so tame and familiar about your camp in the northern woods or in the Rockies, and the other jays so wary? Such variations, of course, have their natural explanation, whatever it may be. In New Zealand there is a parrot, the kea, that once lived upon honey and fruit, but that now lives upon the sheep, tearing its way down to the kidney fat.

This is a wide departure in instinct, but it is not

to be read as a development of reason in its place. It is a modified instinct, — the instinct for food seeking new sources of supply. Exactly how it came about would be interesting to know. Our oriole is an insectivorous bird, but in some localities it is very destructive in the August vineyards. It does not become a fruit-eater like the robin, but a juice-sucker; it punctures the grapes for their unfermented wine. Here, again, we have a case of modified and adaptive instinct. All animals are more or less adaptive, and avail themselves of new sources of food supply. When the southern savannas were planted with rice, the bobolinks soon found that this food suited them. A few years ago we had a great visitation in the Hudson River Valley of crossbills from the north. They lingered till the fruit of the peach orchards had set, when they discovered that here was a new source of food supply, and they became very destructive to the promised crop by deftly cutting out the embryo peaches. All such cases show how plastic and adaptive instinct is, at least in relation to food supplies. Let me again say that instinct is native, untaught intelligence, directed outward, but never inward as in man.

VII. THE ROBIN

Probably, with us, no other bird is so closely associated with country life as the robin; most of the time pleasantly, but for a brief season, during cherry time, unpleasantly. His life touches or mingles with ours at many points — in the dooryard, in the garden, in the orchard, along the road, in the groves, in the woods. He is everywhere except in the depths of the primitive forests, and he is always very much at home. He does not hang timidly upon the skirts of our rural life, like, say, the thrasher or the chewink ; he plunges in boldly and takes his chances, and his share, and often more than his share, of whatever is going. What vigor, what cheer, how persistent, how prolific, how adaptive ; pugnacious, but cheery, pilfering, but companionable!

When one first sees his ruddy breast upon the lawn in spring, or his pert form outlined against a patch of lingering snow in the brown fields, or hears his simple carol from the top of a leafless tree at sundown, what a vernal thrill it gives one! What a train of pleasant associations is quickened into life!

What pictures he makes upon the lawn! What attitudes he strikes! See him seize a worm and yank it from its burrow!

I recently observed a robin boring for grubs in a country dooryard. It is a common enough sight to witness one seize an angle-worm and drag it from its burrow in the turf, but I am not sure that I ever before saw one drill for grubs and bring the big white morsel to the surface. The robin I am speaking of had a nest of young in a maple near by, and she worked the neighborhood very industriously for food. She would run along over the short grass after the manner of robins, stopping every few feet, her form stiff and erect. Now and then she would suddenly bend her head toward the ground and bring eye or ear for a moment to bear intently upon it. Then she would spring to boring the turf vigorously with her bill, changing her attitude at each stroke, alert and watchful, throwing up the grass roots and little jets of soil, stabbing deeper and deeper, growing every moment more and more excited, till finally a fat grub was seized and brought forth. Time after time, during several days, I saw her mine for grubs in this way and drag them forth. How did she know where to drill? The insect was in every case an inch below the surface. Did she hear it gnawing the roots of the grasses, or did she see a movement in the turf beneath which the grub was at work? I know not. I only know that she struck her game unerringly each time. Only twice did I see her make a few thrusts and then desist, as if she had been for the moment deceived.

How pugnacious the robin is! With what spunk and spirit he defends himself against his enemies! Every spring I see the robins mobbing the blue jays that go sneaking through the trees looking for eggs. The crow blackbirds nest in my evergreens, and there is perpetual war between them and the robins.

The blackbirds devour the robins' eggs, and the robins never cease to utter their protest, often backing it up with blows. I saw two robins attack a young blackbird in the air, and they tweaked out his feathers at a lively rate.

One spring a pack of robins killed a cuckoo near me that they found robbing a nest. I did not witness the killing, but I have cross-questioned a number of people who did see it, and I am convinced of the fact. They set upon him when he was on the robin's nest, and left him so bruised and helpless beneath it that he soon died. It was the first intimation I had ever had that the cuckoo devoured the eggs of other birds.

Two other well-authenticated cases have come to my knowledge of robins killing cuckoos (the black-billed) in May. The robin knows its enemies, and it is quite certain, I think, that the cuckoo is one of them.

What a hustler the robin is! No wonder he gets on in the world. He is early, he is handy, he is adaptive, he is tenacious. Before the leaves are out in April the female begins her nest, concealing it as much as she can in a tree-crotch, or placing it under a shed or porch, or even under an overhanging bank upon the ground. One spring a robin built her nest upon the ladder that was hung up beneath the eaves of the wagon-shed. Having occasion to use the ladder, we placed the nest on a box that stood beneath it. The robin was disturbed at first, but soon went on with her incubating in the new and more exposed position. The same spring one built her nest upon a beam in a half-finished fruit house, going out and in through the unshingled roof. One day, just as the eggs were hatched, we completed the roof, and kept up a hammering about the place till near night; the mother robin scolded a good deal, but she did not desert her young, and soon found her way in and out the door.

If a robin makes up her mind to build upon your porch, and you make up your mind that you do not want her there, there is likely to be considerable trouble on both sides before the matter is settled. The robin gets the start of you in the morning, and has her heap of dry grass and straws in place before the jealous broom is stirring, and she persists after you have cleaned out her rubbish half a dozen times. Before you have discouraged her, you may have to shunt her off of every plate or other "coign of vantage" with boards or shingles. A strenuous bird indeed, and a hustler.

VIII. THE CROW

One very cold winter's morning, after a fall of nearly two feet of snow, as I came out of my door three crows were perched in an apple tree but a few rods away. One of them uttered a peculiar caw as they saw me, but they did not fly away. It was not the usual high-keyed note of alarm. It may have meant " Look out!" yet it seemed to me like the asking of alms: " Here we are, three hungry neighbors of yours; give us food." So I brought out the entrails and legs of a chicken, and placed them upon the snow. The crows very soon discovered what I had done, and with the usual suspicious movement of the closed wings which has the effect of emphasizing the birds' alertness, approached and devoured the food or carried it away. But there was not the least strife or dispute among them over the food. Indeed, each seemed ready to give precedence to the others. In fact, the crow is a courtly, fine-mannered bird. Birds of prey will rend one another over their food; even buzzards will make some show of mauling one another with their wings; but I have yet to see anything of the kind with that gentle freebooter, the crow. Yet suspicion is his dominant trait. Anything that looks like design puts him on his guard. The simplest device in a cornfield usually suffices to keep him away. He suspects a trap. His wit is not deep, but it is quick, and ever on the alert.

One of our natural history romancers makes the crows flock in June. But the truth is, they do not flock till September. Through the summer the different families keep pretty well together. You may see the old ones with their young foraging about the fields, the young often being fed by their parents.

GATHERED BY THE WAY

From my boyhood I have seen the yearly meeting of the crows in September or October, on a high grassy hill or a wooded ridge. Apparently, all the crows from a large area assemble at these times; you may see them coming, singly or in loose bands, from all directions to the rendezvous, till there are hundreds of them together. They make black an acre or two of ground. At intervals they all rise in the air, and wheel about, all cawing at once. Then to the ground again, or to the tree-tops, as the case may be; then, rising again, they send forth the voice of the multitude. What does it all mean? I notice that this rally is always preliminary to their going into winter quarters. It would be interesting to know just the nature of the communication that takes place between them. Not long afterwards, or early in October, they may be seen morning and evening going to and from their rookeries. The matter seems to be settled in these September gatherings of the clan. Was the spot agreed upon beforehand and notice served upon all the members of the tribe? Our "school-of-the-woods" professors would probably infer something of the kind. I suspect it is all brought about as naturally as any other aggregation of animals. A few crows meet on the hill; they attract others and still others. The rising of a body of them in the air, the circling and cawing, may be an instinctive act to advertise the meeting to all the crows within sight or hearing. At any rate, it has this effect, and they come hurrying from all points.

What their various calls mean, who shall tell? That lusty *caw-aw*, *caw-aw* that one hears in spring and summer, like the voice of authority or command, what does it mean? I never could find out. It is doubtless from the male. A crow will utter it while sitting alone on the fence in the pasture, as well as when flying through the air. The crow's cry of alarm is easily distinguished; all the other birds and wild creatures know it, and the hunter who is stalking his game is apt to swear when he hears it. I have heard two crows in the spring, seated on a limb close together, give utterance to many curious, guttural, gurgling, ventriloquial sounds. What were they saying? It was probably some form of the language of love.

I venture to say that no one has ever yet heard the crow utter a complaining or a disconsolate note. He is always cheery, he is always self-possessed, he is a great success. Nothing in Bermuda made me feel so much at home as a flock of half a dozen of our crows which I saw and heard there. At one time they were very numerous on the island, but they have been persecuted till only a remnant of the tribe remains.

I

My friend and neighbor through the year,
Self-appointed overseer

GATHERED BY THE WAY

Of my crops of fruit and grain,
Of my woods and furrowed plain,

Claim thy tithings right and left,
I shall never call it theft.

Nature wisely made the law,
And I fail to find a flaw

In thy title to the earth,
And all it holds of any worth.

I like thy self-complacent air,
I like thy ways so free from care,

Thy landlord stroll about my fields,
Quickly noting what each yields;

Thy courtly mien and bearing bold,
As if thy claim were bought with gold;

Thy floating shape against the sky,
When days are calm and clouds sail high;

Thy thrifty flight ere rise of sun,
Thy homing clans when day is done.

Hues protective are not thine,
So sleek thy coat each quill doth shine.

Diamond black to end of toe,
Thy counter-point the crystal snow.

WAYS OF NATURE

II

Never plaintive nor appealing,
Quite at home when thou art stealing,

Always groomed to tip of feather,
Calm and trim in every weather,

Morn till night my woods policing,
Every sound thy watch increasing.

Hawk and owl in tree-top hiding
Feel the shame of thy deriding.

Naught escapes thy observation,
None but dread thy accusation.

Hunters, prowlers, woodland lovers
Vainly seek the leafy covers.

III

Noisy, scheming, and predacious,
With demeanor almost gracious,

Dowered with leisure, void of hurry,
Void of fuss and void of worry,

Friendly bandit, Robin Hood,
Judge and jury of the wood,

Or Captain Kidd of sable quill,
Hiding treasures in the hill,

GATHERED BY THE WAY

Nature made thee for each season,
Gave thee wit for ample reason,

Good crow wit that's always burnished
Like the coat her care has furnished.

May thy numbers ne'er diminish,
I'll befriend thee till life's finish.

May I never cease to meet thee,
May I never have to eat thee.

And mayest thou never have to fare so
That thou playest the part of scarecrow.

INDEX

INDEX

INDEX

INDEX

INDEX

INDEX